OUR TIME TO SAY GOODBYE

A couple's journey through dementia

Ron E Freckleton

To Elena

Enjoy this gift from Andrea.

I hope you like my story

Ron

Ron E. Freckleton (signature)

Our Time to Say Goodbye .... A couple's journey through dementia.

Author   Ron E. Freckleton   2016

Dedicated to

Joanie

The love of my life

Acknowledgements

To Dale Wallace for giving me an honest and encouraging appraisal of my first draft. Dale's advice led me to seek opportunities to improve the manuscript. To all of the wonderful people at the University of Calgary's Continuing Education and On-line Learning departments. Jude Williams the Program Coordinator for Continuing Education challenged me to take the Learning on-line prerequisite course. Professor Sarah Eaton needed lots of patience as I navigated my way through the Desire to Learn experience. Professor Sherryl Melnyk. Sherryl knew I was a writer before I did. Her advice and encouragement gave me the ability to transfer my thoughts into words and truly express myself. My fellow students in Sherryl's Creative Non-fiction course. Their critiques of my work told me that my writing had merit. To Patsy Knudson, the Universities Continuing Educations Program Manager. Patsy introduced me to Simon Rose, my editor. Simons writing experience, proofreading and editorial skills helped me make the book readable.

Really special thanks to our family doctor. Don Stinton. Don's experience, compassion and common sense mentoring made my journey with Joan so much easier. Without his guidance, the road we travelled would have been far more difficult.

I owe a debt of gratitude to the caregivers at Park Place, Chinook Park Care Centre. The care and love they gave unconditionally to Joan, will surely earn them a special place in Heaven.

The families of Joan and myself plus all of our friends will always hold a special place in my heart. Their love and support through the years will sustain me for ever.

I was sitting at Joan's bedside in the emergency department of Rocky View Hospital in Calgary. It was around 10 pm on Maundy Thursday. The doctor on duty sat down beside me.

"You know she's dying," he said. It wasn't a question. "She'll probably be gone within a couple of hours."

Joan died 61 hours later. I was holding her hand. It was 11:11 am on Easter Sunday, April 20, 2014

Chapter One

On the evening of December 15, 2006, Joan and I were at the beautiful home of Jan, the daughter my niece Marg. Jan and her husband Brett were hosting a family get-together to celebrate a very special anniversary. Joan and I had been married exactly fifty years.

The young couple had generously opened their spacious, tastefully furnished home in Elbow Springs, a new sub-division on the western edge of Calgary, to all of our extended family. There were twenty-one family members in attendance. Nieces and nephews and their spouses, along with the grandnieces and nephews with their spouses or significant others, were all there. There were no great-grand nieces or nephews. They were being baby-sat on this special night. Just a few of our Calgary family members were unable to be with us. It would have been even lovelier if some of Joan's immediate family could have attended. Geographical conditions made that impossible since they all lived in England. Yet we knew that their thoughts were with us. Some of them had also called earlier that day.

A small group of our special friends had been in-vited, including three couples, Lucille and Ralph, Jim and Rozzane, and Joan and Gary. We were so pleased when they accepted Jan's invitation. Joan's other special friend, Donna, had been invited, but she didn't like to travel on cold, icy, snowy Calgary roads at night. How-ever, she would see us soon.

It was a memorable evening for Joan and I. The knowledge that we were so loved by our family and friends buoyed our spirits tremendously.

Joan's cognitive degeneration was known only to Joan and myself. Of course, she wasn't aware that I knew her secret. Six months earlier, during a weekend stay at our holiday trailer in Canmore, I confirmed to myself that we were dealing with early onset dementia. Each night, at home in Calgary or at our Canmore mountain retreat, Joan habitually placed the medication prescribed to control her blood pressure on her bedside table. A small pill, it would be ready for her the next morning. On this occasion, a short time after placing the first pill on the table, she placed another one beside it. I quietly pointed out her error. Joan's immediate and explosive outburst startled me.

"I don't have Alzheimer's. I don't have Alzheimer's." Her knee-jerk reaction had accidently released her terrible secret.

"No, Joanie, no you don't," I said, refusing to say the word Alzheimer's. "Just a mistake, you made a little mistake. Everyone makes mistakes."

Joan was distraught. We stood together in the small room. I held her close. She beat on me with tiny clenched fists. I held her closer and I kissed her tear stained face,

"Let me kiss away those tears, Joanie, you don't need to cry."

Her sobbing lessened, her anger subsided. I told her that I loved her, I always have and I always will. She'd just been a little forgetful, something that happens to all of us as we get older. My soothing words seemed to comfort Joan and the sobbing stopped.

There was no reason for me to confirm the deadly truth. If we were to continue living our pretense of a normal life, I had to convince my Joanie that I thought that everything was okay. I did a good job. Joan slept in my arms that night. Her secret was hers alone. I lay beside her, with my forlorn hope that we would have a few more years of love and happiness together.

Chapter Two

On this happy celebratory occasion, surrounded by family and friends, I saw no reason to attract sympathy and cause unneeded concern. Joan and I were content to be the center of attention for the right reason. We were loved.

I could see the happiness in Joan's eyes. I'd seen this radiance many times before, although not recently. She greeted everyone with such enthusiasm, with big hugs for all. She knew it was close to Christmas. Perhaps she was thinking that she should make the most of it.

"Merry Christmas," she replied, to everyone that wished her Happy Anniversary.

This house was full of love. Not just for Joan and me. I could feel the festive ambiance all around us. It pervaded each of the crowded rooms as our extended family greeted each other, some for the first time in a year. Our friends, perhaps a little overwhelmed early in the evening, were soon enveloped in the family circle. Lots of laughs as snippets of our past life were revealed and exaggerated. Joan did most of the exaggerating, magnifying little incidents just to see me blush, then she'd collapse into laughter.

"Look at his face." That was my Joan. I loved her so much.

Amongst the wonderful gifts showered upon us later in the evening was a beautiful framed collage of pictures. Jim and Rozzane had assembled them to remind us of our early vacations in Hawaii. We visited the Islands with this lovely couple for a good number of years, way back in the seventies. What a wonderful keepsake. What memories to share.

Chris, my niece and goddaughter, and her husband, Rob, would later become my go-to people. They'd put together a DVD comprising pictures of Joan and I. The photos taken on our wedding day, Joan looking radiant, me looking just a little bit smug. Why wouldn't I be? I'd just married a wonderful young lady. More pictures of our adventures through the years. At our trailer in Scotland and at our mountain and golfing retreat in Canmore. We viewed all of the pictures on the big-screen TV.

The young ones in the family were amazed and somewhat hysterical to see old pictures of Uncle Ronnie with hair. I reminded them, just to get even, that it was a family trait. My male pattern baldness was in their genes and in their future.

Joan was delighted to see a picture of herself when we first arrived in Canada in early 1973. She was wearing huge Deirdre Barlow glasses.

"Ain't I got style?" she said.

I was moved by the choice of background music Rob had chosen for his picture show. For the early days he'd selected Rod Stewart's rock classic "*Forever Young.*" For the later years, "*In My Life.*" John Lennon's beautiful ballad.

Joan and I sat together in the middle of a huge leather couch, holding hands as we always did, watching on the super-sized screen, breathing in the nostalgia we felt as each picture faded and another wonderful memory took its place. Our own big secret was, at least for now, erased from our thoughts. We were so happy and in love for all of those past years. We will stay in love. I prayed that we would remain happy.

After midnight, the celebration over, Joan and I were at home, safely tucked into our lovely warm bed. Joan cuddled up really close. We talked about how we'd enjoyed the night and how lucky we were to have family and friends that really loved us. Pretty soon, Joan was sleeping, her steady, regular breathing signaled that she would have a restful night.

As I did every other night, I lay awake. This time, instead of being immersed in the fear and dread of our bleak future, I thought of the wonderful life that my Joanie and I had shared. I had so much to be thankful for. The memory of the day I met the love of my life will last forever.

Chapter Three

It was a grey, damp Saturday afternoon in late October. The year was 1954. Six months earlier, three months after my twenty-first birthday, I'd been demobilized from Her Majesty's Royal Air Force. I'd spent two of my three years' service touring half a dozen Near Eastern countries. I was an aircraft mechanic on a mobile fighter squadron, we showed the flag wherever and whenever we were ordered to. I don't know if Malta and Cyprus are in the Near East, I know Tunisia, Libya, Egypt's Canal Zone are. I think Iraq is in the Middle East.

My military experience had been a lot more cushioned than that of two of my three older brothers, Tommy and Frankie. They'd served in the Royal Navy, escorting merchant ship convoys during the war years. Their frigates patrolled the vulnerable Atlantic Ocean or the frigid northern waters between Great Britain and Russia. I remember listening intently as they painted verbal pictures of the fierce cold they endured when they had to chip ice off the superstructure of their warship. To fail in their task would have led to their ship capsizing.

Our dad was in the Navy during the First World War. He was a seventeen years old when his ship was torpedoed in the Mediterranean. They were ferrying mules from Alexandria in Egypt to Gallipoli in Turkey. I've seen the printed record of his service. One page quotes the simple message:

"Ship sunk. Captain died."

Dad had been in the RAF during the Second War serving in our home city of Liverpool. He was a corporal in a team that hoisted barrage balloons into the sky above Merseyside. The balloons were used to deter Germany's mighty Luftwaffe from destroying our city. I don't know how successful they were. I remember the excitement when one of the balloons got loose and knocked Mrs. Hall's chimney off. I was eight years old at the time.

Johnnie, my other brother, was two years older than me and was conscripted into the army on his eighteenth birthday. He spent his two years on Salisbury Plain serving in the Royal Signals. Johnnie left the army in the same month that I joined the RAF.

I was seated on the back row of a bus. It was a luxury coach, hired for the day for a family trip to Blackpool. The parents of the host family, the Walsh's, lived on our street in Liverpool. The kids were all born there, had married, and moved away. When I say moved away, I mean that they moved to different parts of Liverpool. Nobody ever truly leaves Liverpool.

The bus was parked outside the Walsh family home. Five brothers and three sisters, each with a spouse, occupied most of the seats. The noisy conversation produced an atmosphere that clearly signaled that everyone was going to have a good time. I felt privileged that I was one of the friends that had been invited to fill up the remaining seats.

At this point Joan and I hadn't met. We were friends of different members of the Walsh clan. Someone in the family, probably my friend Brian, had arranged, or should I say contrived, that Joan and I would sit together for the trip.

Albert, the second eldest of the Walsh brothers, guided a lovely young woman towards the vacant seat next to mine.

"Joan, this is Ronnie Freck. He's a mate of our Brian. Joan babysits for me and Winnie."

"Hiya."

Joan returned my greetings as she sat down. I explained that my last name was Freckleton. Everyone that knew our family called us the Frecks. It was so much easier.

"My last name is Sandison," said Joan. "It's spelled with an I. My granddad was Scottish."

I wasn't good at one-on-one conversations with young women. I hadn't had much practice. My sisters had taught me to dance, everything from an old fashioned waltz to a tango. I wish they'd taught me some of the other social graces. I was shy, self-conscious, and lacked confidence. How was I going to survive this bus trip? Joan, outwardly self-confident but probably just as shy as I was, soon put me at my ease.

"Do you live around here?"

"Yes," I said, pointing through the rear window of the bus. "There's our house right there. The end one, with the driveway for a car."

Our house was about three hundred feet away. My family didn't have a car, just an ancient van.

The houses on our street, Malmesbury Road, were similar in style to hundreds, maybe thousands, of other homes in Norris Green, one of the huge outer suburbs of Liverpool. In the late 1920s, the City of Liverpool built and rented the new homes to working class family's eager to escape the crowded environs of the inner city. The Freckleton's were one of the first families to settle in our road. We lived in number 7. Johnnie, Sylvia and I were born in the front bedroom. The odd numbered houses were all "kitchen" houses. The downstairs contained a hallway, a front room that we called the kitchen, and a back room, where the stove and sink was, which we called the back kitchen. The upstairs consisted of three bedrooms and a bathroom. We had a toilet situated outside the back kitchen door. It was in an alcove, but I was never sure if it was classified as an outside toilet or an inside one. I suppose it was an inside toilet if we were trying to impress someone. The even numbered houses on the opposite side of the street were "parlor" houses. They had an extra room downstairs. The tenants paid more rent than on our side of the street so we considered them to be rather posh. The Walsh's lived in a parlor house.

I can't pretend to remember what Joan and I talked about while the bus carried us to our destination. I do remember thinking how lucky I was, sitting next to this attractive young lady. Usually so awkward, I found myself able to maintain a conversation. This girl must be really special.

Joan's eyes were the first of her features that grabbed my attention. Big and brown with lovely long lashes. There was a mark on the bridge of her nose. I'll bet she usually wears glasses. She had dark brown hair, not short but not long either. It was curled and waved in the style of one of the latest Hollywood heroines, don't ask me which one. Joan was wearing a little make-up, but she didn't need to wear any. A small trace of lipstick framed what I would call a perfect mouth. I wondered what she saw in me.

Chapter Four

Why Blackpool? It was a seaside resort town a couple of hours drive north of Liverpool. The town, with its huge sandy beach, the noisy fairground with the giant Ferris wheel, the amusement arcades, the myriad of souvenir shops displaying the buckets and spades, inflatable swimming rings, sticks of Blackpool Rock, and 'Kiss Me Quick' sailor hats, attracted holidaymakers from all over the north of England.

The main attractions in the late season in Blackpool were the breathtaking electric light displays. The illuminated tableaux depicting various themes were spaced more or less evenly along the seven-mile long promenade. The prom stretched for the entire length of the town. The local tramcars, buses, and department stores were all similarly decorated. After dusk during the months of September and October the road that ran parallel to the light show would be filled with buses, each jammed with excited occupants, the buses crawling nose to tail as they made their way to the end of the promenade. The buses were crawling but the occupants were usually seated comfortably.

Following a couple of initially awkward then interesting travelling hours for Joan and I, our bus joined the convoy. We viewed the lights, which everyone on the bus thought were wonderful. We were all suitably enthralled by the magic of electric light synchronization.

Other attractions in the town included the busy cafes and pubs. Of course no young person could visit

Blackpool and not venture inside the famous Tower Ballroom, the North of England's Mecca of ballroom dancing.

After viewing the last of the illuminated displays, our group found a large and noisy restaurant pub. We all had a nice meal of fish and chips, accompanied by alcoholic refreshments. Beer for the men and Baby Cham, the latest boutique drink, for the ladies.

Our next stop was the Tower Ballroom. The billboards proclaimed that we should step inside and dance to the melodic tones of the renowned Reginald Dixon and his famous Wurlitzer organ. Reginald's signature tune, *Oh, I do like to be beside the seaside*, was known to all. The incorrigible Walsh family were loudly singing his anthem as we made our entrance.

Joan and I both enjoyed dancing and were very soon on the dance floor. After only one dance we were the very best of friends.

"For this is the Kingdom of Heaven and here on the threshold we stand, pass through the portals now, we'll be immortal now, hold my hand."

Don Cornell's song, *Hold my Hand*, was number one on the hit parade and would remain at the top of the charts for another twenty weeks. Our boisterous group belted out the words as we danced. We were warned to 'Keep it down' or we'd be asked to leave.

The trip back to Liverpool was quiet, except for the ribald commentary from Freddie Griffith, one of my recently married friends. Joan and I were holding hands.

"Look at Joan Sandison and Ronnie Freck holding hands," he remarked. "They'll have to get married now."

I was always a shy person and prone to blushing when teased. I think this convinced Joan that I was a nice guy. She agreed to "go out" with me to the movies the following evening.

We met at the front of the theatre, which was showing *On the Waterfront* with Marlon Brando. Who could forget our first date? I bought a big bag of Maltesers before the movie started. Joan kept popping them into her mouth as the on-screen drama progressed. I think she was as nervous as I was.

Finally, the movie ended. It seemed as though it would go on forever. I was thrilled when Joan allowed me to hold her hand as we walked the short distance to her home. I asked if I could take her dancing the following Saturday night. She accepted and I was ecstatic. We exchanged just one kiss when we said goodbye. I wasn't going to push my luck. On the bone-rattling tram ride home, I was mentally pinching myself. I was convinced that I was in love.

Our mutual love of ballroom dancing lead us to the local dance hall every weekend. Of course, if there was a big band performing at the Grafton, our favorite ballroom, we swapped our movie night for an extra night of whirling around the dance floor. The last waltz always came too early but we enjoyed that dance the most.

Chapter Five

After four or five weeks of dating three or four times each week, Joan introduced me to her parents. Her younger siblings thought it was great. Their Joan had a fella. Joan was the eldest girl. The other children were Maureen, Kathleen, Carol, and Jimmy. Her older brother, George, was six months younger than me and had married his childhood sweetheart, Kitty. They had two children and were living with Kitty's parents. Joan idolized her big brother. George taught her to dance and was her protector against any boyfriends that might venture away from civilized behavior. Jim and Katie, Joan's parents, were a well matched, obviously caring pair. Jim, with his quiet conversational way of speaking, soon put me at my ease. Katie, in a nice new pinny, gently warned the kids to be on their best behavior.

"Now, now." Little Jimmy quietly withdrew his repeated proclamation that the chocolate éclair was his. I relaxed. This was a lot easier than I thought it would be.

Meeting my mum and dad was a different experience. We had a big German shepherd called Bruce, King of Elton. My dad's brother was a breeder and had chosen this name. It looked really classy scrolled on the pedigree registration certificate. Elton was a play on our last name. We just called him Bruce.

Walking into our street, Joan and I were about a hundred yards from my home. It was one of a number of suburban, semi-detached houses, all with neat front gardens bordered by privet hedges.

"Here, Bruce." On hearing my voice, our dog leapt over the five-foot hedge and bounded towards us. Joan's face was a picture, something between terror and absolute terror. Living in a tenement environment all of her life, she'd never got up close and personal to any dog. Bruce jumped up as he reached us. I just had to order him to sit and he sat. My uncle had trained him well.

"Walk," I said.

Bruce then walked quietly beside us. Joan was gripping my arm really, really tightly.

Initially nervous, Joan soon became comfortable with my parents. My siblings Sylvia, Tommy, and John, weren't at home. Lil, Frank, and Elsie were all married with families and were living in their own homes.

"Is your dad Jimmy Sandison? I used to go to school with him and his brother, Willie. Do you remember them, Lizzie? They lived in Netherfield Road."

My parents had grown up in the same area as Joan's dad. There, the ice was broken.

Joan and I started going steady. Yes, that's what they called it then. Going steady, not 'seeing each other.' What the heck does that mean anyway? In Liverpool, at my age, going out with a girl was tantamount to abandoning a masculine lifestyle that was sacrosanct. Going steady with a girl meant that I was ready to almost abandon my friends. Note the word almost. Who would willingly quit the Saturday night get-togethers in Ma Shaw's, our pub adjacent to the Grafton? The camaraderie and the singing, the quality of the latter always improving as the empty beer glasses accumulated on the table. It was a young person's gathering place and where we readied ourselves for a good night of dancing. Joan and I joined our group of friends just for this Saturday night ritual.

The rest of the week we were with each other. We were a couple and that was all that we wished to be.

When Jim and Katie got married, probably around 1932, they started their family in a flat in one of a group of tenements in Soho Street, just a fifteen-minute walk from Liverpool's dockside. After the war, due to extensive bomb damage, they moved to a home on the third floor of one of several newly-built tenement buildings just a half-mile further away from the docks. They still lived there while Joan and I were courting. The reason I mention this is because I had a fitness routine that was connected to our courtship. Whether it was a dance hall night, a movie night, or just a window shopping night, we would always end it with what modern kids would call a 'make out' session in Joan's living room. Nothing hot and heavy since her parents were in the next room. Around midnight each evening we'd hear the last tram car rattling and screeching around the corner of Islington and Shaw Street.

My late night fitness workout would start by kissing Joan goodnight, galloping down three flights of stairs, and dashing out onto Westbourne Street, which ran parallel to Shaw Street. I then had a 500-yard sprint to catch the tram as it turned the next corner. The penalty for missing the tram was a six-mile walk back home to Norris Green. It should have been an Olympic event.

Chapter Six

One year after we met, Joan and I became engaged. I don't remember popping the question but I do remember buying the ring from Samuel's Jewelers on Church Street. It didn't take long for Joan to choose the ring. I think she'd probably picked it out when window shopping with friends before I'd even asked. Needing to save some money and find a place to live, we decided that the wedding would take place in December 1956, six months after Joan's twenty-first birthday.

When I did the traditional thing of asking Joan's dad for permission to marry, I wasn't relieved that he didn't offer any opposition, although it never entered my head that he would. I remember Jim asking me when the wedding would take place.

"In fifteen months."

"Why are you waiting so long?" he asked.

In later years I often reminded Joan that her dad seemed to be in great haste to get her off his hands.

"How much did you pay him?" was always her stock answer.

We both had a sense of humor. They say of Liverpool that you have to have a sense of humor to live there. Liverpool had the reputation of being a tough town. Its humor, usually edgy, self-depreciating, aimed at mockery of a friend or slanting any situation to obtain a laugh, was endemic. Everyone seemed to be willing to trade humor for the difficulties in life that we all encountered at times.

"If you paid your rent two weeks in a row, the police knocked on your door wanting to know where you got the money."

That old joke sometimes had a ring of truth to it. Dodging the rent man was common practice.

Joan loved to laugh. Her style was to pretend to be angry or fierce then her big grin would break out. We all knew that we'd been had once again.

Our courtship was a fun period, involving less time with our friends and more time with each other. We enjoyed a week-long holiday at one of the Butlin's holiday resorts. This was in Pwllelli in North Wales. This type of holiday was popular with young people and families in those days. There were lots of things to do, such as dancing, drinking, good food, or organized sports. Best of all, it was a cheap holiday, out of town and away from work.

On our first evening away from home, I was less than a gentleman, I plied Joan with drink, hoping for the opportunity to have my wicked way with her. She drank me under the table and I spent the night with my head in the toilet.

The night before our wedding, Joan partied at the local pub with her sister Maureen and her friends. Maureen was a little younger than the legal drinking age of eighteen but nobody noticed. I was supposed to go to a different pub for my bachelor party but I never got there. I was busy fitting new carpet in the little apartment that we'd managed to obtain. I needed to get our first home ready for our new life together. It was midnight before the job was finished. The upside was that I would be sans-hangover for the next day's ceremony.

Chapter Seven

Christ's Church, Norris Green, where I was christened almost 24 years earlier, was crowded at 3 pm on Saturday, December 15, 1956. The ceremony was conducted by the Anglican minister that had baptized me, the Reverend Cyril Henry Winstanley.

One of my lasting memories of that very special day will always be seeing Joan walking down the aisle on the arm of her loving dad. The organist was playing *Ava Maria*. Joan looked absolutely radiant. My brother and best man, Tommy, was by my side, both of us looking sharp in new suits. Joan wore a stylish high-necked, long-sleeved wedding gown and cradled a bouquet of beautiful flowers, her proud dad at her side. They were followed down the aisle by her seventeen-year old sister, Maureen, Joan's only bridesmaid.

As the service proceeded, the vicar seemed to put special emphasis on the words, 'Let no man put asunder.' He was aware that Joan's parents had been told by their parish priest not to allow our wedding. The fact that Joan and I were of different Christian denominations meant nothing to us. We knew that we belonged to each other and that was all that mattered.

Joan had been educated at the local convent school. Too much contact with religion had moved her away from the dogma she'd been taught in her childhood. She told me of the trepidation that she and her fellow students felt when they heard the jangle of Sister Mary Margaret's cross and chain as the tyrant swished her way towards the classroom. Miss McGrath the headmistress and her indiscriminate cane were even more menacing.

"Do you know your catechisms, child? No? Hold out your hand."

Our wedding was typical of most weddings in our town. The reception was self-catered at the local co-operative hall. There was lots of last minute preparation but everyone willing to help. There was always someone who seemed to know somebody that could get us a deal on just about everything that we'd need. It seemed that every person we'd ever known was invited. One of Joan's uncles tended the well-stocked and well-patronized bar. He did a wonderful job. For the whole evening, everyone had their drinks dispensed in proper fashion. Shortly before midnight, as the last of the guests were preparing to depart, Uncle John, our bartender extraordinaire, quietly collapsed. He sort of dissolved onto the floor. He wasn't ill, just a little bit tipsy. He seemed to have dispensed more than just a few drinks for himself.

It's funny, the weird little things that we remember about major events in our lives. At that time there was a bus strike and only a skeleton service was being provided. Just after midnight, Joan and I joined the queue waiting for what would be the last bus. It was already crowded as it trundled to a stop.

"Just room for four more," said the plaintive voice belonging to the blousy, blonde conductor.

Joan and I were fifth and sixth in line.

"Sorry, Ron," said the conductor.

She was a regular customer at our store and had recognized me.

"Sorry, Ron," mimicked a drunk behind us in the queue.

I was so glad that he didn't persist, I'd have had to respond to his provocation. Joan and I walked for twenty minutes to our new home, holding hands, happy that everything had gone well. All of our guests had re-mained good humored, a noteworthy achievement at any Liverpool wedding. It was an auspicious start to our new life together.

A couple of weeks later we repeated our marriage vows at a side altar of Joan's church. It was mainly to comfort Joan's mother. As Joan's brother, George put it,

"It'll get the priest of our back."

The ritual would also assuage any feelings of guilt, however misplaced, that Joan might encounter later in life.

Our first year of marriage was filled with new and exciting experiences for both of us. At a time and place where newlyweds had difficulty finding a home of their own, most couples usually started out living with one of their families in crowded and tense conditions. Fortunately, we'd managed to find a small flat over a va-cant shop. It was on Heyworth Street, part of an area that hadn't yet been fully reconstructed after the ravages of the wartime bombing of Liverpool. There were lots of empty spaces where bustling shops or pubs used to be, hard evidence of the Luftwaffe's lack of accuracy. The docks were a good three miles away. Our front door, our only door, opened into the shop's back yard but that was fine. We had our own place and we knew just how lucky we were.

Joan's first cooking efforts were, to say the least, below par. I learned a lot about diplomacy and she soon learned to be a really excellent cook. In later years, her early culinary efforts were something else about which we often shared jokes.

Our apartment wasn't far from the corner store that I managed for my dad. Within walking distance of Joan's family home, it was also on the bus route to the silk stocking manufacturing plant where Joan was employed. Her job was to repair faulty product, enabling it to be sold as second grade. She described herself as the invisible mender.

A year or so after we moved in, after having to tolerate the vacant shop being transformed into a ripe smelling fruit and veg shop and later into a creepy undertaker's parlor, we decided that we would look for a nicer place, one that would be our 'forever home.'

Chapter Eight

14 Cornett Road, Aintree was our new address. It was a small terraced house on a very quiet street not far from the famous race course. Joan loved it. We made the few changes that we thought were necessary, including a new glass paneled front door and a polished stone front step that Joan's dad, a terrazzo floor professional, installed for us. Our first 'real' home was perfect. Joan's newly acquired decorating skills made it even more wonderful.

Joan started work in the office of a local gaming company. Her new job was closer to our home and also paid better wages.

I bought a pre-owned Lambretta scooter to make my commute to the shop easier. We had lots of laughs with the scooter. I wasted many hours tinkering with its little engine that I knew nothing about. Joan refused to ride it when we were going uphill, claiming, truthfully, that she could walk faster. She also refused to wear a helmet.

"I'm not going to ruin my hair."

After five years in Cornett Road and eight years managing my dad's store, a job that entailed long working hours, little job satisfaction, and very little free time, Joan and I decided that we should move on and find more challenging occupations. Joan's dad wasn't happy when we told him that I'd applied for a job that would take us away from Liverpool.

"If you want to leave town, get a job over the water."

He meant Birkenhead, the town on the opposite side of the River Mersey. It was just a short trip on the ferry from Liverpool or a fifteen-minute drive through the Mersey Tunnel. He didn't want me taking his lovely Joan off to distant places. My dad wasn't pleased either. I'd offered to buy the shop but he didn't wish to ignite any resentment with my siblings and he also wasn't interested in retiring at that time. However, I left his employment with his blessing and no hard feelings.

Chapter Nine

In January 1963, two days after my thirtieth birthday, I joined Navy, Army and Air Force Institutes (NAAFI) as a trainee store and shop manager. The organization had the mandate to supply just about everything that British military personnel and their families would need for daily living.

Leaving Joan at Cornett Road, I moved through a small number of shops on military bases in Northern England. I spent a couple of months learning the system, always returning home to Joan each weekend.

I was asked to manage a store and shop on an army base close to Stratford-upon-Avon. It would be for a three-month trial period. The shop was a modern building with living accommodation above it. The Army base was in Long Marston, while the NAAFI shop was near the village of Lower Quinton, just a mile away. Nearby was another village, Upper Quinton, which was south of Lower Quinton. I don't remember a hill. No wonder the Romans got confused.

After a month, Joan joined me. We now had our first car, a sporty-looking green Austin A40.

The next two months were wonderful. It was early spring and we toured Shakespeare country each weekend. Most weekday evenings were spent exploring the many quaintly-named towns and villages, each with at least one excellent hostelry. Moreton-in-Marsh, Shipston-on-Stour, Bidford-On-Avon, Royal Leamington Spa were some of the towns in the area. The smaller villages all had their thatched roofed cottages with beautiful gardens. There was always a village green, its mandatory bench usually occupied by at least one old gentleman keeping his eye on things. I'll bet if we'd stayed long enough we'd have spotted Miss Marple looking for the clues that would solve her latest mystery.

The probationary period over, I was appointed manager of the NAAFI Store and Shop at Beachley College, a training unit of the Royal Engineers. Situated on the border of Gloucestershire in England and Monmouthshire in Wales, it was near the small border town of Chepstow. The college was located in what we would come to think of as one of the most beautiful places in the UK.

Joan accepted the opportunity to be one of my cashiers. We were starting a working partnership that would last for ten years.

Our first couple of nights were spent at the appropriately named Beachley Hotel. Situated next to the car ferry terminal, which was actually just a dock and a toll booth, the hotel was a couple of hundred yards from the main gate of the college. The busy ferry took tourists and other travelers to Bristol on the south shore of the River Severn's wide estuary.

Our hotel room looked out onto the construction site of the new Severn Bridge. At the time we didn't give a thought to whether we'd still be at Beachley when the bridge was completed. It was officially opened by Queen Elizabeth in 1967.

Mr. Richmond was our District Manager and my new boss. A rather stern Welshman, I never knew his first name. He advised me to find a temporary place to live while our employer found us a permanent home in the area. It took us less than a day to find a beautiful apartment on a farm in the picturesque Wye Valley.

Our new landlord was a tenant himself. The farm was on land belonging to the Crown and was part of the Duchy of Cornwall's estates. The farming couple were very friendly and unobtrusive. Their three very active young sons, age about twelve, ten and eight were however very obtrusive, but in a really good way. Most evenings after work, the boys would knock on our door.

"Mr. and Mrs. Freckleton, will you come down to the river and catch fish with us?"

Sometimes they were asking us to play cricket, rounders, football or whatever activity they thought we should share with them. Their energy seemed boundless. We had to convince the boy's parents that we enjoyed interacting with their offspring and we really did. We had as much fun as the boys. We just got tired more quickly.

Sheep usually grazed in the meadow next to the house. They were always attracted to Joan as she hung out our washing to dry.

"Ronnie, come and chase these sheep!"

The farm's two Welsh sheepdogs would never come to her rescue. If the sheep were in the meadow, that's where they were supposed to be, as far as the dogs were concerned. Mrs. Freckleton can fend for herself. The dogs had fun each morning as we set off in the car, scampering around, snapping at each wheel. I'm pretty sure they were just teasing us. They must have guessed that we were city people.

We spent a very enjoyable three months on the farm. For those twelve weeks we lived in Wales and worked in England.

Chapter Ten

NAAFI found us a lovely modern home in Tutshill, a couple of miles from our workplace. It was in a newly developed area. Most of the residents were of our age group. Some were military and others were civilians working at the college.

We very quickly developed friendships with neighbors and with my new staff members. Joan's outgoing and friendly personality soon dispelled any doubt that they may have had that their new manager would be a suitable replacement for their previous boss.

We became close friends with our head cashier, Marg Rafferty and her husband, Chips, who was a sergeant-major. My status allowed me to be an honorary member of the Sergeants Mess and the four of us spent many happy hours there. We attended formal dinners, weekend social dances, or just hung out for a quiet drink. I half-remember one formal dinner that we attended. It was special but I can't remember why. I had to rent a tuxedo, ruffed white shirt, bow tie, and a cummerbund, the whole enchilada. I was the only civilian in the Mess that night and the only male without medals on his chest. I stuck out like a sore thumb. I gave quiet thanks to God that my friends in Liverpool couldn't see me. Joan giggled each time she looked at me.

Marg and Joan became members of the college ladies rifle club and competed against other lady's teams. We spent a few weekend mornings tramping around fields to the shooting ranges of the various clubs in the area.

When Marg and Chips had a baby son, Russell, Joan and I were both very honored to be asked to be his godparents. The Sunday baptism was performed in the college chapel and the happy celebration was held at the Sergeants Mess. It didn't surprise anyone when, a little later in the afternoon, the chaplain's car was seen on the hallowed parade square, a place where no one was allowed to walk, never mind drive a vehicle. The car was moving somewhat erratically. Start, stop, start, stop again. The chaplain was giving Joan her first driving lesson. Breathalyzers weren't in use at that time and that was a really good thing. In the following weeks, Joan continued her driving lessons with a professional instructor and passed the test after her second attempt.

Viscount Victor Brooke, the son of Field Marshal Lord Allanbrooke, was one of the college's company commanders. He and Joan shared the same zany sense of humor. Our NAAFI shop was near the rear edge of the parade ground. On some mornings, using an electronic megaphone as he drilled his troops, he would bellow:

"Good Morning, Mrs. Freckleton."

The whole camp would hear the greeting and wonder what the heck was going on. Yes, we thought Captain Brooke was a little quirky. Not Robin Williams quirky, more like Mr. Bean.

He enjoyed chatting with Joan when he made occasional purchases at the shop. On one visit, he told Joan that he was going to Brighton to spend time with his mother. Naturally, Joan asked him not to forget to bring back a stick of rock. This is a traditional thing for anyone visiting a sea-side resort to do. Shops in every resort town sold a hard rock mint candy with the resort's name incorporated through the middle of the baton-shaped treat. However, Captain Brooke had no idea what Joan was talking about. A couple of weeks later he arrived at the NAAFI shop with Joan's stick of rock. It was in a Fortnum and Mason's bag. He'd persuaded his dear mater to make the purchase at the most exclusive shop in London.

Chapter Eleven

Our time at Beachley enabled Joan and I to enjoy personal growth and a quality of life that we couldn't have attained had we stayed in Liverpool. Now officially a management team, we were able to challenge our potential without being fearful of what other people thought.

Of course we still regularly visited our parents, family, and friends in Liverpool. We still loved the city and everything about it but we no longer considered it to be our home.

We both enjoyed working in the NAAFI Shop. The diversity of the job meant that there was always something happening. One day I'd be ensuring that the Commanding Officer had Wheat Flakes for breakfast.

"Wheat Flakes, Mr. Freckleton, not Corn Flakes. Corn is for chickens."

The next day I'd be expediting the delivery of 300 athletic supports.

"Can't have the boys damaging their vital parts. Mr. Freckleton."

It was always Mr. Freckleton. Only our friends knew our first names.

On one occasion, the president of the Wives Club asked me to move our rack of paperbacks to a less visible area.

"The Bishop is visiting tomorrow. He wouldn't be pleased to see those lurid covers on some of the books. Actually, the covers don't even relate to the stories." She must have read these titillating novels to be aware of this information.

The wife of one of the junior officers was a kleptomaniac. We had very diplomatic procedures that prevented her from doing what she was wont to do. Another wife was a nymphomaniac. The staff told me that I had to send our store man if she ever needed a delivery to her home. Joan thought that was a good plan. I pretended that I thought so too.

Part of NAAFI's responsibilities was to supply all of the food requirements for the cadets and the living-in staff. The quantity of each product that was required was calculated by multiplying the amount that one person was entitled to by the number of persons actually being catered for. It wasn't as complicated as it seems.

The Officers' and Sergeants' Messes ordered whatever they wished. They didn't have any bureaucratic restrictions placed on how they spent their funds.

The shop was stocked and operated in a similar fashion to a High Street grocers and our inventory included wines, spirits, and beer. We also had a comprehensive non-foods section. Our customer base was the living-out staff. These mostly comprised married officers and non-commissioned personnel living with their families in the surrounding communities. Civilians working for the college were also encouraged to shop our store. However, our NAAFI shop was off-limits to the cadets.

In 1966, we won a hundred pounds for the best Christmas display. Our competitors were all the NAAFI shops of varying sizes at the military bases in our region.

The Head Office instructed that we should use the cash for a staff celebration. At Joan's instigation the staff decided that we should use the money to entertain some underprivileged children. I contacted the Social Services in Newport, an industrial town in South Wales. It was about a forty-five-minute drive from Beachley. They could provide a bus, a driver, a social worker, and enough underprivileged kids to fill the bus. There would be six seats left for Joan and me plus four of my staff. We would be the chaperones. We decided that the youngsters would enjoy a Christmas pantomime, *Aladdin,* at the Empire Theatre in Newport. Our prize money paid for the tickets. The Sergeants' Mess donated enough funds for each child to be given a generous goodie bag.

What a night we had. If you've ever been to a panto you'll know that there's always lots of audience participation. Our group were louder than anyone.

"Oh no, I didn't!" the villain proclaimed from the stage.

"Oh yes, you did!" every kid in the place would yell back.

The villain would repeat his protest and the kids would yell even louder. This kind of interaction occurred every time the villain was on stage. I remarked to the social worker that our kids were rather boisterous. She replied that they were underprivileged, not underdeveloped.

Back on the bus, the kid's goodie bags were distributed. I thought some of the youngsters were going to burst with excitement. I'm sure my staff were as happy as Joan and I. The kids had a night they would remember for a while and so did we.

Chapter Twelve

After five very enjoyable years at Beachley, the opportunity to advance our careers arose. We were asked if we would take over a larger establishment, on a Royal Air Force base in the Highlands of Scotland. We decided that we should make the move.

It was difficult to say goodbye to all of our many friends. We were so reluctant to leave our lovely home and the shop and store that had been the focal points of our lives for almost five years.

Our long trip to the Highlands began on a cold and wet Friday morning in February. We were headed to the small town of Forres in Morayshire. It was situated on the south shore of the Firth of Moray, between picturesque Inverness and Aberdeen, the Granite City.

We planned to spend part of the weekend in Liverpool then continue the journey north on Sunday. Our furniture was packed and would arrive in Forres on Monday morning.

The rain turned into heavy snow as we traveled north to Liverpool. Stopping for lunch at a service area restaurant seemed to be a good idea. The problem was that everyone else on the highway had the same notion. After enjoying a long lunch waiting for the snow to abate, we emerged to find the huge parking lot filled with cars. Every car was completely covered in wet snow. We had no idea which one was ours. A number of cars were cleared of snow before we eventually found the right one.

On Sunday morning we said goodbye to Joan's parents with a promise to visit as soon as possible then set off on our six-hour journey. Although it was another grey February day it was very enjoyable drive. First, we drove the express motorway that ran through the length of Northwest England. It continued over the border into the south of Scotland. One of the directional signs read 'Gretna Green, Turn Right.'

"We don't need to, we're already married."

Joan was referring to the tradition of young English couples running off to Scotland to get married. In the eighteenth century it was decreed that twenty-one was the minimum age to be married in England. In Scotland, the age of consent was much younger. Gretna Green was the closest place to the border where the wedding ceremonies could be performed.

The motorway continued through Robbie Burns Country. I practiced my phone Scottish accent with some of Burns' poetry.

"Oh what a gift that God could gie us. To see oursels as ithers see us" Joan was less than impressed so I tried again.

"Wee sleeked timorous cowering beastie, oh what a panic in thy breastie."

Joan threatened to jump out of the car.

The highway narrowed into a trunk road. The A96 would take us all the way to Forres. Bypassing the major towns, the long and winding road took us through some lovely small hamlets and villages.

Closer to our destination we experienced the Highland glens. The awesome sight of purple heather in huge patches by the roadside and throughout the glens was spectacular.

Arriving in Forres just before dark in the early evening, we booked into one of the hotels of our new home town. Our first taste of Highland hospitality was a wonderful mixed grill prepared specially for us by the owner of the hotel. It was called high tea and it really was splendid. Our host put an electric heating pad in our bed.

"You might find it a wee bit chilly in the morning." That was a huge understatement. It was freezing.

After breakfast, we drove over to Hillcrest, Orchard Road. Our new home was a lovely modernized 100-year-old stone built house with a high pitched slate roof and a small front garden. A separate garage, freestanding washhouse and workshop were each built with the same stone as the house. Together they separated the back yard from a huge rear garden. The house and the garden were both well maintained. Owned by NAAFI, the house had been the home of the previous manager, who had obviously been an avid gardener.

Our moving van arrived almost at the same time as we did. Our first day was spent unpacking our stuff and arranging then re-arranging the furniture.

Early on the following morning, we were wakened early by loud rattling noises followed by piercing squawks. The noise was coming from right above us. I discovered a little later that a thin coating of ice had formed on the slate roof and converted it into an almost vertical skating rink for the local gulls. Attempting to land at the top, they slid down on their backsides to the eaves troughs below. The squawking and screeching appeared to indicate that the gulls enjoyed the fun.

Chapter Thirteen

RAF Kinloss, a large airbase on the Moray Firth, was the site of our new posting. The NAAFI Shop and Store was located close to the main gate.

Mr. Ross, our new District Manager, was a soft spoken Highlander and was waiting for us when we arrived at the store the next morning. He introduced us to the staff as he showed us around the premises. A large mobile shop was parked outside the back of the store. This was used for servicing the needs of the families at Lossiemouth, a Royal Naval Air Station a few miles east of Kinloss. The mobile shop's operation was part of my new responsibilities.

The staff, about twenty in total, were mostly local. Some were spouses of RAF personnel, living in married quarters or in rented properties in the area.

As we were introduced, we had some fun trying to understand each other's speech. The highland dialect was a little difficult for Joan and I to understand, but our Liverpool accent was the real impediment. We knew immediately that we'd have to learn to communicate in language that could be understood.

Our staff were all friendly but cautious of the new boss. They'd held the previous manager, a local

man, in high esteem. He'd been asked to take early retirement. I never asked why. Joan and I were aware that
we had to earn their trust, especially because we were
from England. We knew that it wasn't going to be easy.

My office manager, Margaret, was a very soft-
spoken, gentle lady and was happy that her new boss
asked her to continue doing her job as she always had.
She'd been fearful that I'd want to make big changes.
The rest of the staff quickly adapted to my management
style. I was once described as a benevolent dictator. Of
course, Joan's friendly personality and quick wit acceler-
ated the 'getting to know everyone' process.

I served three years in the RAF when I was conscripted in 1951. I was an aircraft mechanic, serving
mostly with a fighter squadron in the Near East. I was
familiar with ranks and protocols that were very different
from the Royal Engineers at Beachley.

With the help of our staff, Joan and I learned how
to run the shop and store efficiently. Pretty soon we were
comfortable meeting the challenges that our new opportunity had brought us.

We found that our new highland friends, at first
cautiously polite, were really genuine. They took some
time assessing us then they accepted us, making us feel
right at home.

Not long after our arrival, we were invited to the
wedding reception of one of our staff members.

"Hey Boss, will you take a half-and-half with
me?" Jock, my mobile shop driver, wasn't talking about
coffee and cream. He meant a half-pint of beer and a
small glass, half full of whisky. How could we risk the
consequences of a refusal? We made our exit as soon as

we deemed it to be polite. Too many half-and-halves could only lead to embarrassment.

On the following Monday morning, I was asked why Joan and I were seen holding hands as we walked along the High Street on Saturday evening. I think we were holding each other up!

Morayshire is Scotch whisky distilling country. Many of the famously named single malts were born in the area. On our first visit to a local hostelry we learned two things about scotch and scotch drinking. Behind the bar, the shelves were full of what seemed to be every brand of scotch ever produced. I ordered two scotch and the good humored bartender, also the owner, raised one eyebrow.

"What brand?" he asked.

It seems that it's customary to name the scotch you require. Nobody orders two scotch. I settled for two Johnny Walker Black Label. As I splashed a little soda water into each drink, my new friend raised his other eyebrow.

"You have a headache in the mornings?"

"Yes, doesn't everybody?"

"It's the bubbles" he said. "If you have to put anything into your drink, just a little water is best."

All this in the broad dialect of the region. It was a pleasant and educational start to our evening.

Chapter Fourteen

At Christmastime in our first year, we were invited, along with all of the other department heads, military and civilian, to the Station Commander's home. It was a beautiful old house situated on the edge of the airfield's runway and close to the road leading to the village of Findhorn.

Early in the evening, the guests seemed to be slightly uncomfortable in the presence of Group Captain Severne. He was also an equerry to Prince Charles. The host circled the large room offering his guests refreshments from a tray full of drinks, scotch of course.

"Scotch, Mrs. Freckleton?"

"Yes, please, sir. No ice".

All the drinks contained ice.

"Not a problem," said the Group Captain.

He removed the ice from one of the glasses with his fingers then handed the glass to Joan. I suppose that sort of broke the ice.

Mrs. Severne was a lovely, mature, down to earth lady. One day the following summer, she came into the shop. We called it a shop but it was really a small supermarket.

"Mr. Freckleton, I must tell you about yesterday."
I was intrigued.

"Why don't we go into my office and you can tell me."

It seemed that Prince Charles had visited them for dinner the previous evening. He was, at that time, boarding at Gordonstoun, an upper-class school that was geared to educating young male adults, the focus being rigorous, outdoor activities. The school was just a few miles from Kinloss.

Before dinner, the Severne's chatted with Prince Charles on the lawn of their lovely house. Every airfield has rabbits and they were doing what rabbits are wont to do, just a couple of yards away. The randy rabbits were attracting the attention of lots of tourists walking by. Prince Charles didn't merit a single glance. He was almost within touching distance but the tourists never knew.

Joan's impish sense of fun often meant that I'd sometimes be the butt of her jokes. A small number of young officer's wives, feeling slightly self-important, would occasionally complain about trivial matters to Joan. Always respectful, Joan would ask if they wished to speak to the manager. I'd then be summoned to the cash desk. Standing beside Joan at her desk, I'd apologize for the shop's perceived shortcomings. Simultaneously Joan would be pinching my bottom, out of the sight of our soon to be placated, customers.

One afternoon, two young, fresh-faced pilot officers were perusing the large selection of wines that our shop stocked. It really was a comprehensive display. We supplied the Officer's Mess, the Sergeant's Mess and the other ranks' club. In addition, we fulfilled the alcoholic needs of everyone on and off the base.

"May I help you find a suitable wine, gentle-men?" They looked at me somewhat disdainfully. How could I possibly help them?

When I joined the RAF and after I'd completed my training as an aircraft mechanic, I was posted for a few months to the RAF College Cranwell. The college was the RAF equivalent to the Army's Sandhurst or the US military's West Point. My job was servicing and re-pairing the light aircraft that the cadets used as they learned the flying portion of their curriculum.

I'd noticed that the wings on the officers' tunics were brand spanking new.

"I see you've got your wings. What school did you graduate from?" They mentioned one of the lesser flying schools.

"I was at Cranwell myself," I replied.

Their deference was immediately noticeable.

"What would you recommend with poached salmon?"

They didn't know that I was the guy that repaired the damage that novice pilots often inflicted on their fly-ing machines.

Chapter Fifteen

The closest army base to Kinloss was Fort George, an ancient fort between Nairn and Inverness. It was only a thirty-minute drive from our NAAFI. The fort was built by King George II after the Battle of Culloden in 1746. His army defeated the Jacobite's of Charles Edward Stuart, also known as Bonnie Prince Charlie to the romantics.

Its northern buttresses facing the Firth of Moray, the fort was perched high above the surrounding bare landscape. A huge portcullis gate ensured that intruders couldn't enter unseen, the fort must have been a difficult bastion to invade. The garrison was always occupied by a Scottish regiment. Currently, the fort housed the Gordon Highlanders, an infantry regiment with a glorious history. They recruited most of their soldiers from the working class areas of Glasgow. These were real fighting men.

The NAAFI shop was situated about a half-mile down the road leading from the fort. John the manager of the shop called me.

"The Queen's visiting the troops today, come on over."

Her Majesty's visit was expected to end soon. Her car had to pass the NAAFI shop. I joined a small group of NAAFI staff and military families, less than two dozen of us in total. Standing next to me was a small, ruddy faced boy about ten years old. He was scruffy, in short pants, with his stockings falling down to his ankles.

"Be sure to wave to the Queen." I told him.

He simply scowled, scuffing his boots into the ground. I assumed that perhaps he didn't care for my English accent.

Within a short period, the Queen's car was sighted. It was exiting through the gate of the fort and our anticipation grew more intense. As the car approached our little group it slowed down to a slow walking pace. The Queen was smiling and gave us all the Royal wave. She seemed to make eye contact with each of us. A couple of years earlier I'd seen the Queen when she officially opened the Severn Bridge. However, I don't think she would have remembered me.

"Wave to the Queen," I said to the little boy.

He stuck his hands deeper into his pockets.

"It's na the Queen."

"Sure it is, wave."

"No. It's na the Queen."

The Queen's car, now clear of our little group, gathered speed and left us behind. She was probably on her way to her family's summer home at Balmoral, less than a two-hour drive from Fort George, an hour and a half if her driver puts his foot down. Perhaps she'll slip off her shoes and have a short nap, she's had a long day. Our little group, loyal subjects all, were content in our good fortune. We'd seen our gracious Queen up close.

"What made you think it wasn't the Queen?" I asked my urchin.

"She did'na have a tiara!" he shouted.

You have to imagine his rich Glaswegian accent to really appreciate the humor.

Chapter Sixteen

Our home was situated in Scotland's finest tourist area. We were just a couple of miles from the beach. A lot of our free time was spent exploring our new playground. Deciding to do the tourist thing, we bought a small holiday trailer.

On most Saturday mornings we hooked it up to the car and away we'd go. North to John O'Groats, west to Inverness or Loch Ness, east through the quaint fishing villages to Aberdeen or south to Aviemore and the Cairngorm mountains. We had so much fun, just the two of us, driving the narrow roads, towing our 'wee caravan.'

On one of our trips we were driving the narrow road south of Loch Ness. As we drove up a steep hill, a large tour bus turned the corner in front of us. The bus was obviously too big to reverse on the narrow road. I backed my vehicle to the nearest turn off. In the UK these are called lay-bys. I unhooked the trailer. The lay-by was just a small gap in the roadside, with insufficient room for both car and trailer, so I proceeded to reverse to the next lay-by. When I reached that, the bus was able to proceed. It stopped as it drew level with my car. All of the passengers were American tourists and gave us a huge ovation. A couple even got off the bus to shake my hand.

Chapter Seventeen

We stayed at Kinloss for five, very eventful years, visiting our families in Liverpool a number of times. We were also visited by family and friends who rightly thought that we should share our lovely home with them, if only for a little while.

When we went south to visit with family, we routinely visited with Joan's parents, a quick hello to my parents then we'd head to St Helens, a few miles from Liverpool. That's where Maureen, Joan's younger sister, and her husband, Bill, now lived.

Saturday night at Sherdley Park's Cricket Club was always a fun time. Lots of dancing, drinking and laughter. We met Gloria and Ray, a married couple, who the same age as Maureen and Bill. They also lived on the same street. After closing time, we'd continue the party at Maureen and Bill's place until Joan and I would retire to the spare bedroom.

An early morning game of 'I Spy' was always the mandatary start to Sunday. This was with their two kids, with Lesley on Joan's side of the bed and little Billy on my side. Later, a leisurely and expansive brunch cooked by Bill the professional chef fortified us for our long journey north. Around one o'clock, it was time for big hugs and the familiar farewell phrase.

"See you soon."

Chapter Eighteen

It was only fitting that our first group of visitors to our highlands home were Maureen, Bill, their two kids, and our mutual friends from St. Helens, Gloria and Ray. We led our guests in doing the things that tourists do. We spent time at the beach of course, although swimming was out of the question. The water was much too cold for the ladies.

We visited the famous battlefield at Culloden. A very somber place and a lot smaller than one would imagine. The stunted trees were monuments to fallen warriors. Each tree was festooned with ribbons left in tribute from descendants of the fallen of both sides of the conflict. It was the last major battle ever fought on British soil and also the bloodiest.

We toured the dank passageways and the battlements of Castle Urquhart. The ancient fortress was perched high above the rocky north shore of Loch Ness. The kids had their cameras ready, just in case Nessie showed up.

Lots of pleasant hours were spent in our lovely back garden. Maureen and Gloria lay on recliners, both desperately anxious to get a golden tan. The kids played on the swing or tried to climb the fruit trees. Bill, Ray, and I depleted my beer supply and Joan did her best to ensure that France's wine industry remained viable.

Our holiday finale was a complete shambles. Maureen stayed home to take care of the children. She was the smart one. The rest of us took off for what was supposed to be an early evening trip on one of the local fishing boats.

At the quayside in Findhorn at 6 pm, the scheduled start time of our trip, we were informed that the boat was involved in a rescue effort on the Firth. Our trip would start when it got back. Common sense told us to skip the fishing and go home.

"No, we'll wait."

Common sense should have insisted.

It was 8 pm when the boat docked without excitement. The rescue was a minor incident that another boat had sorted out. It was just before nine, almost dark and getting cooler, when we cast off.

The fishing boat was about eighty feet in length and broad beamed. Lockers on both sides of the forecastle served as seats for the would-be fishermen. A crew of three middle-aged locals, our group of five, plus three young men were on our way for a couple of hours of good fishing. Joan and Gloria couldn't be persuaded to bait the hooks.

"I'm not touching those smelly things," said Joan.

"I'm freezing," Gloria added.

It was getting colder. We'd expected our fishing trip to be over before dark, so we hadn't brought heavy jackets.

After a few minutes, the crew informed us that we'd reached a good fishing area and would soon be reeling them in. The boats engine was stopped. The lights from the boat gave us a small area of illuminated calm, inky black, water around us. No moonlight. The cloud cover ensured complete darkness except for our circle of light. Without the noise of the engine, every-thing was quiet.

"What's that plopping sound?"

It wasn't sea monsters coming to take a look at us, just recently emptied beer cans, tossed into the water from the three young men. They hadn't even bothered to put their lines into the water.

There was no excitement from reeling in the big one. There was no excitement at all, suddenly,

"I've got one."

Bill was hauling in his line. It must be a big one.

"We may have to lash it to the side of the boat."

I was thinking of Hemmingway's *The Old Man and the Sea*.

There wasn't much of a struggle bringing it in. Bill claimed it was eight inches long. I scoffed, estimat-ing the size to be less than six inches. We hadn't discov-ered the shoal. Bill's whopper was the only fish caught on that trip. The boat owner claimed that our lack of suc-cess was very unusual. I was more than a little skeptical. The young men were still drinking their beer. Gloria was joined by Joan with her lament.

"I'm freezing."

Soon, but not soon enough, we were heading back to shore. Once docked, we were in the car, heater on full blast, heading for home. A few minutes and a couple of scotches later, Bill the professional chef, was trying to fillet his catch of the day.

"Get that stinky thing off my kitchen table."

Joan was not a happy camper.

Chapter Nineteen

My eldest brother Frank visited. I think it was in late August, 1970. He was accompanied by his lovely wife, Joyce. Their two sons, Frankie and Mark, had grown into young men and preferred to stay in Liverpool with their friends. Frank and Joyce would spend a few days with us before heading off to tour the rest of the Highlands. Their trip would include John O'Groats, the most northerly town in Great Britain. A few years earlier, they'd visited us when we were at Beachley. On that trip, they were on the way to Land's End, Britain's most southerly town.

Early on their second evening with us, leaving Joan at home to prepare supper, we walked the headland behind the beach on the east side of Findorn Bay. The village of Findhorn was on the west shore of the bay.

After a few minutes of strolling, we turned and retraced our steps. It was almost suppertime. As we neared the bay I noticed a small group of children playing in the water close to the shore. One of the children, a young girl, appeared to be in distress. Frank and I rushed down into the shallow water. The girl, around twelve years old, had stepped into a deep hole in the water near the shore. She was out of her depth and in difficulties. Frank, slightly ahead of me in our race across the beach, stepped into the deep area, grabbed the girl and handed her to me. I was about thigh-deep. Taking the girl, I deposited her onto the shore. When I looked back at Frank, he was struggling to remain afloat. He was wearing a heavy, thick woolen sweater. It was becoming waterlogged and dragging him down. I grabbed him by the scruff of the neck, keeping him afloat until he was able to get a foothold and get himself back into the shallower water.

A young adult couple were with the children, although they weren't the parents. I think the young woman was an aunt. They'd been preoccupied and had not noticed the drama until we were in the water. After receiving profuse thanks, Frank and I departed to my car. We'd both taken off our sodden sweaters and shirts. I drove the short distance to home bare chested.

The following day, the local newspaper's headline read: *Unknown men rescue girl.*

We had a laugh about the headline and the comment that followed. *"It was thought that both men may have been foreign.because they had strange accents"*

I guess our Liverpool Scouse accent would be foreign to some people. Frank and I enjoyed our anonymity. We didn't need anything more than the thanks we received from the young girl.

My office manager Margaret, knowing that Joan and I had my brother visiting, guessed that we were probably the foreigners. Her guess was reinforced by someone asking her.

"Why was your boss driving through town without his shirt on?"

She kept our secret although she begged me to meet with the girl's grandfather, whom she knew. He wanted to thank us. I told Margaret that we didn't need any extra thanks. She respected my wishes and the local mystery would remain unsolved.

Chapter Twenty

Our last group of visitors was from Calgary, Alberta, in Western Canada. My older sister Lil had migrated to Calgary in the mid-sixties with her husband, John, and their three young daughters, Sylvia, Margaret, and Christine. Joan and I had travelled from Beachley to be at the dockside when *The Empress of Canada* left Liverpool and transported them to their new homeland.

When planning their upcoming holiday in Liverpool, they asked if they could also visit us. Naturally we accepted. We didn't know that they were bringing three of the girls' Canadian friends plus my mum and dad from Liverpool.

That was a wonderful week. I arranged that Joan and I would take our vacation time while they were with us. Tacking on an extra week's holiday enabled us to spend some time in Liverpool with them.

Joan and I enjoyed our conversations with Sylvia, Marg, and Chris. The three toothsome pre-teens that left Liverpool in 1966 were now beautiful young ladies. Each of them full of the self-confidence that their time in Canada had nurtured.

Chris, my godchild, was the youngest and was the athlete. Although small in stature, she excelled in basketball, traditionally a tall girls sport. Marg, always the quiet one, was engaged to be married to a young man from the Okanagan. Sylvia, after being a volunteer while she was at school, was now the Volunteer Coordinator at a Seniors Care Centre. Her warm outgoing personality guaranteed that she'd be successful.

Lil, my sister and the girl's mother, was very special to me. Of the seven siblings, she was the middle one and I was the second youngest. Sylvia was the baby of the family while John was two years older than me.

When Lil was just a young pre-teenager during the war years, she had the onerous task of bringing up her three youngest siblings. Our mother was working full-time at a munitions factory. Dad was in the RAF, two older brothers, Tommy and Frankie, were in the Royal Navy and my eldest sister, Elsie, worked for a parachute manufacturer.

"You're not the boss of me."

"Oh yes, I am!"

Our relationship wasn't always adversarial. We had fun watching her demonstrate her tap dancing and singing routines. Lil had joined a juvenile dance group, the Hylda Fallon Chorus. They would be performing in the Aladdin pantomime at one of the local theatres.

"Ching Chong Chinaman, Mushy. Mushy Sad."

We all sang along. This now, totally unacceptable, politically incorrect ditty was fun for the children of the 1940s.

It wasn't until much later that I realized that our Lil had helped form our lives and we were, what we were, because of her love for us.

Chapter Twenty-one

A few months prior to the Canadian's visit, I'd entered a retailer's contest. It was possible to win one of ten five-pound notes, one of three color televisions, or a Rover 2000 car. The competition, sponsored by the British Potato Marketing Board, asked the entrant to list, in the correct order, six reasons how potatoes could help a person slim. The reasons were printed on the entry form, one just had to find the correct order. There was also a tie-breaking slogan that the entrant had to submit on the form. This was a slogan of ten words or less containing the words 'New British Potatoes.'

Each retailer was allowed one entry form for every 100lb of new potatoes they sold during the period of the promotion. Being the supplier to the base and a pretty good salesman, I convinced the Catering Officer that he should buy new potatoes instead of the usual crop. My salesmanship resulted in sixty-four entry forms to submit. I separated what I thought were the three best reasons from the three worst reasons and permutated the numbers. The result gave me sixty-four different combinations. It took a week to dream up what I thought would be a good slogan.

On the day we left for our holiday, confident that I'd win something, I told Margaret, she was still, my long-serving, right hand in the office, that there would be a letter arriving for me from the Potato Marketing Board. She was to open the letter and call me to tell me what I'd won. On Monday morning, our holiday over and no phone call from Margaret, I returned to work somewhat disappointed.

"I didn't get a letter?"

"Aye, you did,"

"Did you open it?"

"Aye, I did."

"Did you read it?"

"No."

"Why not?"

"I was afraid."

With that, she handed me the letter. I read the contents and discovered that I'd won the car. I gave Margaret a big hug, called Joan into the office, and gave her an even bigger hug after I told her the wonderful news.

Those potatoes changed our lives forever. We phoned Liverpool to tell our families of our good fortune. I promised John and Lil, who were still in Liverpool, that we'd sell our current car and use the proceeds to take a holiday in Calgary. Our Canadian vacation was planned for the following summer and we'd stay with Lil and John.

The presentation of the prize a couple of weeks later was a wonderful experience for Joan and I. The ceremony took place at the Potato Marketing Board's location at Edinburgh's Royal Ingleston Showground.

After Joan received a lovely bouquet of flowers from the wife of the Minister of Agriculture, the Chairman of the Board presented me with the keys of the beautiful, royal blue, Rover 2000. My slogan had been:

'New British Potatoes with the Old Country Flavor.'

The Chairman remarked that my slogan would be used to market our British potatoes into Europe's Common Market. I was given the opportunity to drive the car for a couple of laps around the race track.

What a day!

Chapter Twenty-two

Our three-week holiday in Calgary was everything we expected and more. The family's friends that we were introduced to greeted us with such enthusiasm. It was as though we'd known them forever. We met Paul, Marg's fiancé, a studious young man, who worked for IBM.

Amongst these friends were a group of young men from Liverpool. Lil and John had met a couple of the youngsters, Harry Jones and Tony Johnson, a few years earlier when the young men were recently arrived immigrants. Harry and Tony were participants in soccer games that John helped coach. Lil's motherly instincts drove her to invite them to Sunday dinner, a meal that was always special in Liverpool. These young men probably missed Sunday dinners as much as they missed their parents.

For the next couple of years, the number of guests steadily increased as more young men from Liverpool were invited to the Torley's Sunday dinner. This group of young ex-pats would remain friends of the family forever, a lasting tribute to Lil and John's hospitality.

During our trip Joan and I visited the Calgary Stampede, the greatest outdoor show on earth. That's how it was publicized and that's what it was.

Driving through the magnificent Rockies, John and Lil took us on a week-long tour of British Columbia. We visited the huge lakes and fruit orchards in the Okanagan Valley. We also met Paul's parents, who lived in the small town of Winfield, close to Kelowna. Joan and I marveled at the variety of fruits and vegetables that Paul's parents grew on their spacious property. The searing high summer heat of Osoyoos made us determined to find a motel with a pool that night.

Lil, John, and the girls pulled out all of the stops, making sure that we'd have a vacation that we'd never forget. We never would.

Joan and I were really impressed by how polite and friendly everyone seemed to be. Joan loved the huge shopping malls. The supermarkets were also so much bigger and the variety of products far superior to the UK. The staff members even put the groceries in bags that they gave us at the checkouts.

Chapter Twenty-three

Too soon, we were on our flight home. Just a couple of hours into the flight, we decided that we should emigrate. There was no big discussion. Admittedly we were probably influenced by our wonderful vacation, but we made the decision together.

I wrote to one of the leading supermarket chains in Calgary, requesting employment as a grocery clerk. They responded that I had a position with them as soon as our immigration was approved. Lil and John were our sponsors. Nine months later, after medical examinations and administrative interviews, Joan and I would be allowed to enter Canada as landed immigrants.

I informed our employers at NAAFI of our decision and although they expressed their regret and a hope that we'd reconsider, they gave us their blessing. The Kinloss hierarchy were similarly regretful. Group Captain Severne had moved on a couple of years earlier. The RAF Station Commander was now Group Captain George Chesworth, who was also the Lord Lieutenant of Morayshire. He presented us with an RAF Kinloss plaque and a signed photo depicting Joan and I receiving a pewter quaich from Mrs. Chesworth on behalf of the Kinloss Wives Club.

A quaich is an ancient drinking vessel. It is used in more modern times in ceremonies connected to Robert Burns suppers. Joan and I were honored to receive such thoughtful gifts and gratified that our work at RAF Kinloss was so appreciated.

Once again we were saying goodbye to a wonderful support group. This time it was our staff at Kinloss. We never dreamed that leaving these lovely people would be so difficult.

In later years, whenever Joan and I reminisced about the wonderful happenings during the five years that we spent in Scotland, our thoughts always went back to our first Halloween in Forres.

We were at home, in the front room, a cheerful fire in the hearth. It was our first experience of 'trick or treating', Scottish style. First came the boisterous young lads. They danced on the doorsteps, trying to be closest to our offerings, each giving us a huge grin as he received his quota from our doled out goodies. Then off they'd scurry, in a hurry to get to the next house.

"Thanks missus, thanks mister," they yelled from halfway down the path.

It was after the first rush of urchins had disappeared that we heard a gentle tapping on the front door. There were two young ladies, the older one probably eleven years old, the little sister, a year younger, both with quiet little voices.

"Trick or treat?"

I guessed that they were sisters. They had similar facial bone structure and both were wearing similar costumes, poke bonnets and shawls. I imagined that they fashioned the look from an illustrated Christmas card or perhaps from a picture of a long gone, great-grandmother. They resembled two diminutive and charming 'wee wifies.'

Joan invited the girls to share the warmth of the front room. In 1968 there was no fear instilled in kids.

None of the dire 'don't talk to strangers' warnings. Grown-ups weren't nervous about interacting with children either. We gave them their treats and they thanked us.

"Would you like a treat?" the older one asked.

"Yes please."

We didn't know what was coming next.

"We'd like to sing a poem," she said, her Highland brogue pronouncing the last word as 'poeyem.'

"What's it called?" I asked.

"The Old Rugged Cross."

They launched right into the beautiful hymn. Their quiet little voices, were crystal clear and filled our front room. Joan and I sat, enthralled. As the two little angels sang all of the verses, Joan and I were moved by the quiet confidence displayed in their performance.

They thanked us again as we ushered them to the door and we thanked them. They'd treated us to something far more valuable than our candy treats. Yes, it was another very precious memory that would last forever.

Back in Liverpool, sadness tempered our excitement as we said our goodbyes to our families and friends. Joan and her family shed more than a few tears before we left for the airport. We departed from Manchester Airport at 10 am on Monday, April 23, 1973, three months after my fortieth birthday.

Chapter Twenty-four

After having our immigration papers processed and a long layover at Toronto Airport, we arrived at Calgary around 8 pm, local time. Seventeen hours was a long time to be travelling, but Joan and I, eager to start our new life, weren't fatigued.

In the Arrivals area, we were overwhelmed by the enthusiasm of the family's greeting and by the joyous reunion as we trundled our luggage cart through the

doors. Lil and her family, having gone through the immigration process themselves, knew that this was an occasion that we wouldn't soon forget.

Marg and her new husband, Paul, had made a special trip to Calgary just to be there to greet us. They'd recently married and were living in British Columbia. Lil and John lived in an older house in Crescent Heights in the north-west quadrant of Calgary, just a fifteen-minute walk to the city center. The view of the downtown was spectacular. Of average size by Canadian standards, the Torley's house was huge compared to number seven Malmesbury Road. Chris and Sylvia each had their own rooms upstairs. Lil had prepared the basement suite for Joan and me.

"It's yours for as long as you wish."

We stayed with the family for two or three weeks. In the middle of our stay, less than ten days after we'd left Liverpool, we received the tragic but expected news of my mother's death. We were all equally sad-dened. The girls had lost a beloved grandmother. Joan and John had lost a mother-in-law that they loved. My grief was somewhat tempered by the memory of our poignant farewell to my mam. Before we left the UK, Joan and I had visited with my mother. She was termi-nally ill in Catherine Street Women's Hospital in Liver-pool. I assumed that her cancer was in the pelvic area. None of the family wished to go into details. My mam went to great lengths to convince us that everything was fine. She told us how she'd enjoyed her visit to the fam-ily in Canada just a couple of years earlier and how much she envied us because we were setting off on a great adventure. She'd travelled to lots of holiday desti-nations in the previous ten years.

My dad hated taking time off from his business and his social connections in town, so mam, deciding that enough was enough, took off with her friends or her sister, sometimes just on her own. She saw most of Eu-rope, including Ireland. She had consoling words for Joan and I.

"Get off and have some fun. Don't worry about me. I've had a good life, go and enjoy yourselves."

She really meant it. There was no self-pity in her voice. She had one closing comment.

"Ronnie, I told you, the old bugger's going to outlive me."

My mam could still raise a laugh. She was refer-ring to my dad. A couple of years earlier he'd been diag-nosed with terminal prostate cancer.

On the morning after we received our devastating news, just before noon, our Canadian family visited the Anglican Cathedral Church of the Redeemer. Although the church was in the middle of bustling downtown Calgary, it was the quiet place that we needed to celebrate our mam's life.

The south wall of the church, to the side of the altar, was mostly occupied by huge stained glass windows. Slowly the cathedral started to flood with brilliant light. The sun was hitting the windows and distributing its rays onto our little group. We were sitting in the front pews, close to the altar. Uncanny? No, just our mam saying goodbye.

The last time I'd been in a cathedral was in 1945. Back then mam took Johnnie, Sylvia, and me to Liverpool's Anglican Cathedral. She was giving thanks. Our family was intact when World War II ended.

Chapter Twenty-five

Joan and I found ourselves an apartment close to the Torley's. We negotiated a fifty-percent rent reduction in exchange for acting as the on-site managers. This Canada really was the land of opportunity.

It was just an eight-suite building so our building supervisor's job wasn't too onerous. Collecting the monthly rent, keeping the building and surrounds tidy, plus making note of anything that needed reporting to the owner. Easy-peasy.

I started work in the supermarket on the Monday after we arrived in Calgary, I experienced a huge culture shock. My major handicap was my managerial past. The first lesson was to forget the past. I had to learn how to do my job and learn how to do it fast. Speed in job completion seemed to be the major concern. Get the product on the shelves fast. Supermarkets demand high volume sales. You can't sell it if it's not on the shelf. I certainly learned what the word hustle meant.

Purchasing a used car was the next priority. This was a Mercury Comet, a nice car with an automatic transmission, something new for me. What was I going to do with my left foot? No clutch to ease in and out. My purchase was influenced by John. His car was virtually identical to mine except that his was a Ford Maverick.

I failed the mandatory Canadian driving test twice. The examiners were befuddled when I thanked them and drove away. Possession of a British driving license gave me a six months' grace period.

Within a month, I did something that I knew that I'd do, sooner or later. I drove my car into a one-way street. I was driving east but on Sixth Avenue Calgary's downtown traffic drives west. I was lucky. Traffic was light and I spotted an alley before I reached the next intersection so extreme embarrassment was averted.

Not all of our first experiences in Calgary were so dramatic although one was tragic. Joan and I attended a 'Welcome to Canada' house party at the home of a friends of the family. Quick to learn local customs, I took along a fifteen-year-old bottle of Glen Morangie's finest single malt Scotch whisky as a gift. It had been given to Joan and I by the management of the famed distillery. I cried inside as I pretended to be amused to see Canadians adding all sorts of mixes to their scotch. Soda water, tonic water, Seven-up, cola, even orange juice. Damn Sassenachs!

Chapter Twenty-six

Joan found a job at a tourist-oriented gift store in the city, a week after I started at the supermarket. Her new bosses, Marj and Stan Kirkham, had recently opened the store. They also bought a pipe and cigar specialty store in the same small complex of shops on the ground floor of the Calgary Tower. Both stores catered to travelers using the rail station attached to the Tower. Local office workers, along with tourists from all over the world, helped the two stores to be profitable.

When it was built in the late sixties, the Husky Tower, as it was then called, was the tallest building in Calgary. Our niece, Marg, Lil and John's middle daughter, was employed as one of the elevator operators. Her job was to describe the Tower's virtues as the elevator whizzed the tourists to the observation platform or to the revolving restaurant. Sadly, Marg's job came to an end when an automated voice took over. The price of progress.

Marj and Stan were wonderful employers. It didn't take Joan long to catch on to the 'funny money.' She settled into her new job very quickly. Joan's strong work ethic was appreciated and it was only a short time later that she was trusted to run the store for short periods without supervision.

Our first experience of real Canadian hospitality came just two weeks after Joan started working for Marj and Stan. They took us to the Jubilee Auditorium to see

Johnny Cash. After the show we had supper at a nice restaurant. It was a really lovely evening. Marj said it was
their way of saying 'Welcome to Canada.' It sure topped
violating a treasured bottle of single malt!

Shortly after Marj and Joan became friends they
decided that they both needed to learn to swim. Enrolling
in a class entitled *Absolutely Terrified*, they spent a number of evenings at the local swimming pool. When the
course finished they were both accomplished swimmers.
In retrospect, it was fortuitous that Joan was now comfortable with aquatic activities. They would play a huge
role in our lives later.

As Joan enjoyed her job more, I became less en-
amored with mine. After some weeks of regular day
shifts, I was rotated onto the midnight shift. Stacking
grocery shelves in the middle of the night did not sit too
well with me. Joan was also uncomfortable having to
spend the nights alone.

I answered an ad for a temporary, part-time employee to help set up a new wholesale cash and carry
outlet. When I reported for an interview in the early
evening, the manager, Mr. Bill Hall, introduced himself,
asked a couple of questions, then put me to work. Keeping my job at the supermarket was important. As a new
immigrant, I needed to feel secure and they were paying
me a good salary. I worked with Bill for a couple of
hours each evening. Chatting as we worked, we discovered that we had similar backgrounds. He had worked in
his dad's store and was born in the Highlands of Scotland.

After a couple of weeks, Bill asked me to join his
team on a full-time basis. I accepted his offer to meet the
salary that I was already receiving. I gave two week's

notice to the supermarket manager. He was very gracious.

"If things don't work out, please come back."

I thought he was being very magnanimous, considering that I'd worked for him for less than six months.

Bill and his lovely wife, Bunny, soon formed a real, lasting friendship with Joan and I. We also became very close to Bill's office assistant Lucille and her husband Ralph. Lucille had transferred from the main office a couple of months after I joined the company. I knew that I'd made the right career move. Joan was pleased that I wouldn't be working any graveyard shifts.

Chapter Twenty-seven

In early September of our first year in Calgary, we moved out of the apartment and purchased a nice home in a gated mobile home park in the north-west of the city. Lil and John purchased the place next door.

Cascade Park was a really vibrant community, with lots of activities, a beautiful clubhouse, a swimming pool, a hot pool, and a social and dance each month. Once again we were making lasting friendships.

After one of the monthly dances, our group of friends partied in one of the homes. The hostess played on a Hammond organ. It was a birthday gift from her husband. Being a novice, her renditions were modestly good. Joan, who in our twenty years of marriage, had never told me that she could play piano, whispered to me.

"I can play better than that."

"If you can, I'll buy you one of those for Christmas," I said.

I thought it was a safe bet but she really could play beautifully.

I hid Joan's new organ at Lil and John's place and surprised her on Christmas morning.

I took up golf, something that I should have done in Scotland, the birthplace of golf. I learned my golf on Sunday mornings with John, Al, and Jim, plus some

other men in our group. We played at one of two munici-
pal golf courses, wherever we could get a tee time. My
early efforts were somewhat pathetic, my self-esteem
taking as much of a beating as the poor golf ball that I
was hitting far too often. I rarely lost a ball. I never hit it
far enough to lose sight of it. When water came between
me and the hole, my supply of golf balls instantly depleted. On those occasions I always managed to hit a reasonable shot right into the middle of the pond. I rationalized that I didn't actually lose the ball. I knew exactly
where it was.

John and our new friends were always very patient with me. They needed to be. Golf is a hard game to
learn when you're over forty years old.

"Why do they ring those church bells just when
I'm trying to putt?"

Chapter Twenty-eight

In the late summer of 1975, Joan and I took a trip to Liverpool. I was eager to let Joan's family know that we were both enjoying our life in Canada. It was a nice, two-week visit, we stayed with Joan's parents. Although we'd only moved to Calgary a couple of years earlier, we hadn't lived in Liverpool for more than twelve years. I'd always thought that the majority of Liverpool people are, to say the least, very insular and my opinion was confirmed during this trip. We were having a Saturday night family get-together at a pub close to Joan's old home. Late into the evening, I met someone I hadn't seen in more than twelve years. He lived near the corner store that I used to manage for my dad.

"Hi Ron. How are you?" he asked. "It's been a long time. What have you been up to?"

Ready to spend a little time describing our new lifestyle and speak of the opportunities our new homeland was providing, I replied.

"Joan and I moved to Canada."

I was amused by his response.

"That's great. How did Everton get on tonight?"

It was Saturday night. It appeared that, as far as he was concerned, if it wasn't about football, Everton or Liverpool, it wasn't worth talking about. Who cares about Canada or wherever?

Another experience provided me with an anecdote that I still love to relate to my Canadian golfing friends. Joan and I both had large extended families. We'd really upset someone if we didn't look in on them. I needed a day off from the visiting and all of the oft-repeated greetings.

"Lovely to see you. Would you like a cup of tea? When are you going back?" Joan had the solution.

"Why don't you go golfing?" My Joan was a genius. Just after the morning rush hour, I set off in our rented car. Heading in the general direction of one of Liverpool's famous golf courses, I got lost. I then spotted a man waiting at a bus stop.

"Could you tell me where the golf course is?"

Had it been that long, away from Liverpool? I had no idea what he said. I didn't understand a single word. I steered the car towards the direction his outstretched arm indicated. Our twelve years away from Liverpool had, of necessity, diluted our accents. I hadn't realized that our understanding of the local patois would be similarly affected.

Eventually, I saw the signage and the short gravel driveway led onto a large car park containing just one car. It was parked close to an old manor house, which I assumed it was the club house. I could see part of the golf course but couldn't see any golfers. Wandering around the apparently deserted clubhouse, I was approached by a rather portly gentleman. He was short with a close clipped moustache, his dark, vested suit just a little crumpled. Probably the club secretary, I thought. My previous experience with the military prompted me to guess that he was a retired junior officer. His voice provided confirmation.

"May I help you, sir?"

I explained that I was visiting from Canada and would just love to play a round of golf on his wonderful course.

"I'm terribly sorry sir, it's Wednesday, lady's day." His was the only car in the parking lot and there wasn't a soul on the golf course. It was lady's day. I wouldn't be golfing this course today. Neither would any other gentleman golfer.

Not to be deprived, when I returned to Joan's parents' home, I called the Royal Birkdale course.

"How soon can you get here?" was the response to my request.

"About forty-five minutes."

"I'll book you in for a 1:30 tee time."

I informed him that I hadn't brought my own clubs.

"No problem, we'll fix you up."

The Royal Birkdale Golf Club was a short distance from Southport, every Liverpudlian's favorite seaside resort. The Evertonian's loved it too. It was less than an hour's drive from Liverpool. The long-established golf course, famous for its degree of difficulty and picturesque surroundings, was on the rotation circuit of courses that were hosts to the Open, the world's most prestigious golf tournament. It was never referred to as the British Open.

When I arrived, I was surprised to see that there was little activity. I could see a few golfers some distance away. A young man greeted me as I walked into the pro shop.

"Mr. Freckleton, welcome."

He fitted me up with a set of clubs.

"I've put a few balls in the bag."

"I'm going to need them. I'm just a novice."

"Best take some more then, you will need them"

There was a heavy emphasis on 'will' as he stuffed another half dozen balls into the bag. He apologized, saying that he wished that he could accompany me but had another commitment. Handing me a scorecard, he told me that I should be sure to keep it and take it back to Canada.

"The Open is being played here next year. I'm sure you'll want to know how you did against Jack Nicklaus."

My total cost was ridiculously small. I'd have gladly paid four times as much.

"Not many people on the course," I remarked.

"No," he explained. "There's an interclub tournament today. Most of our members are at another course."

I was in heaven. It was a beautiful sunny day and the slight wind coming off the Irish Sea cooled the temperature. Just a few thin clouds drifted across the pale blue sky. No one was present to watch me making my clumsy tee shots or count my mulligans. This was wonderful.

Using the map on the scorecard, I muddled my way through each hole. Predictably, I lost a large number of balls. Imagining that I was playing the Open, I wondered if any of those professional golfers could make quadruple bogeys on most of the holes and still felt as happy as I did? I made par on the short seventeenth. What an achievement. No, I didn't dance around the green, although I certainly wanted to.

Getting back to Liverpool in time for a late supper, there was just the one question from Joan. It was directed to her mam and dad.

"How are we going to get that smile off his face?"

A couple of days later, it was time for us to go back to Calgary. Joan and her family said their tearful goodbyes. Not wanting to go through a second instalment, we took a cab to the airport. Goodbyes are so difficult.

On our long trip home, yes, Calgary was our home now, we agreed that it was nice to see everyone. However, it was nicer to go home.

Chapter Twenty-nine

Al Carey, one of my golfing buddies, and his wife Tillie, a lovely, older couple in our community, also became our good friends. We were developing so many lasting friendships. Al was a mechanic at a local garage and serviced our car. It felt good to know that we had someone we could trust looking after it. He was from the small town of Swift Current in Saskatchewan, which Al referred to as Speedy Creek. He and Tillie owned a holiday trailer in a small park in Canmore, a mountain town about an hour's drive west of Calgary. A long-time member of the town's golf club, Al made sure that there was always a game of golf on the agenda whenever we visited.

After a few visits to their idyllic spot in the mountains, Joan and I thought it would be a good idea to join them. We bought a trailer, parked it next to Al and Tillie's place, and proceeded to enjoy the wondrous Canadian Rockies on our doorstep. I was accepted as a member of the golf club at the start of the following season. For many years, we spent lots of wonderful summer weekends and made some lasting friendships in beautiful Canmore. Through those same years I witnessed the transformation of our lovely rustic nine-hole golf course into a really wonderful first-class, eighteen-hole golfing experience. It really was classy.

Our members were not the rich, toffee-nosed snobs found in some of Calgary's newer private courses. Some of our older guys took great pride in the fact that they helped build the original course. I remember one old boy, fishing through his wallet and producing his somewhat tattered, founder member card. It was number one.

Another really old guy I golfed with was Lou, a retired Canmore coal miner. He was a wonderful golfer, although he could no longer see where his shots landed. Once we were playing a par-four, both of us playing from about an equal distance. He played his third shot, I played my fourth. I walked to my ball, which was on the green.

"That's my ball," Lou declared.

"No, I watched it land," I replied. "Look, there's my logo."

"I don't understand," says Lou "I hit a good shot."

He sure did. After about five minutes searching we found his ball in the hole. Another ho-hum birdie for Lou. I two-putted for my usual double bogie.

"Have you lived in Canmore all of your life, Lou?" I asked.

"Not yet."

While I was a working stiff, I golfed most weekends at Canmore and some evenings in town. As a retiree, I golfed two or three times each week on weekdays, mostly with our Canmore Senior Men's Club, a real fun bunch of old guys. Ninety-nine percent of them were better golfers than me. The other guy hardly ever showed up. I had the most fun when I golfed on Monday afternoons. The routine was that Joan and I would aquazice in the morning then drive out to the trailer in Canmore. I'd pop over to the golf course for a quick round. Nine holes or eighteen holes, whatever I had time for. Sometimes, if it was a really nice day, I'd convince Joan to come with me. I'd join up with the first available group that was less than a foursome. Tourists were my favorite golfing companions. They were always in awe of our Rockies and the wonderful golf course that I called mine. I used to tease them.

"Just think, I have to play golf here every day."

It was a lie but it was such fun.

In 2003, I was honored to become a Life Member of the golf club. A combination of reaching seventy years of age and being a member for twenty-five years entitled me to golf exempt from all fees for the rest of my life. I made a vow to myself that I would live long and prosper.

Chapter Thirty

Jim and Rozanne were another couple in our group. Jim was one of our Cascade golfing group. They moved into the Mobile Home Park just a month or two before we did. Jim was a Scot and Rozanne was of Ukrainian extraction. I learned this at one of our monthly community dances. Late into the evening, I'd told an inappropriate Ukrainian joke.

"100-percent Ron," she replied, when I questioned whether or not she was kidding.

We became close friends. Jim was a barber and an avid Montreal Canadiens fan. Who wouldn't be friends with his barber? As long as Jim didn't try to convert me into being a Habs supporter, we could remain friends. Rozanne was the assistant to the President of the University of Calgary.

In 1981 Jim and Rozanne organized a surprise party at their home on our twenty-fifth wedding anniversary. Joan and I thought that we were going to their place for a quiet drink. All of our Calgary friends, including Lil and John, were hiding in the basement when we arrived. A lovely surprise indeed.

In April 1987, they, along with Lucille, Ralph, and my staff at the Cash and Carry, organized my retirement party at a local community center. Jim got Joan and I to the venue by telling us that we were going to a friend's wedding reception. Joan knew the plan. She made sure that I was looking my best.

All of my staff, most of the company's upper management team, my family, including my sister Sylvia and her husband Bill from Vancouver Island, lots of my customers and salespeople that were also my friends, were in attendance. Everyone that I wished to be there was there. What a lovely surprise. It was all a bit overwhelming for me. Joan loved it. I think she had a part in the planning.

Lucille told me later that it had been an invitation-only event. They could have filled two halls with the people that wanted to be there. I thought that was very flattering. Ralph filmed the party. He was obviously a pipe fitter and certainly wasn't a movie director. We continued to enjoy watching the movie for years. What should have been Ralph's out-takes provided the most hilarity.

At the 1975 Community Christmas party Jim and Rozanne suggested that we should accompany them on a winter holiday in Hawaii the following March. Considering the long and very cold winters in Calgary, it didn't take us too long to think about it.

Chapter Thirty-one

Joan and I fell in love with Hawaii. We decided that it was our island home, or at least our wannabe home. Every year from 1976 to 2001 Joan and I vacationed in our paradise. Sometimes, for a month, sometimes for three weeks, a few times just for two weeks, always in the months of February, March, or April. Our first half-dozen visits were with our good friends, Jim and Rozanne.

On our first trip, Wardair lived up to their promise that our holiday would start as we boarded their plane. It was a charter flight. Every passenger was ready to exchange the freezing cold of Calgary for the soft humidity and warm sunshine of the Hawaiian Islands. The outstanding in-flight service, delicious meals, and abundant complimentary drinks added to the wonderful, almost euphoric, excitement.

I'll never forget our first look at the Islands as the pilot banked the plane on our approach to Honolulu Airport. It was around noon, Hawaii time. The varying hues of the ocean. White speckled azure blues turning into differing shades of green as the waters became shallower closer to the shoreline. The extinct volcano, Diamond Head, was unexpectedly green. The gentle slopes of the Pali Range, the symmetry of the Punchbowl, the ships and boats cluttering Pearl Harbor and the clusters of high-rise buildings of Honolulu were all evidence that Hawaii was more than sandy beaches and mai tais.

After we'd touched down and the doors of the plane were opened, Joan and I experienced the humidity of Hawaii for the first time. It really did make the skin feel softer.

Jim and Rozanne, both sun worshippers, were seasoned visitors to the islands. They'd vacationed there a number of times before. On our first trip we stayed at a middle-of-the-road hotel in the center of the tourist trap that was Waikiki. Jim and Rozanne guided us through all the touristy stuff that tourists do.

The following year, and for a couple of years after that, golf clubs were part of our luggage. Sometimes all four of us golfed. More often, it was just Jim and I. We played a number of different golf courses, some great, some only excellent. I remember the four of us golfing the Pali course and it rained when we were half-way through the round. We'd spent a few bucks on the green fees so we decided that we'd complete our game. The ordeal over, we made our dripping entrance into the clubhouse, where our soggy and sorry-looking quartet found ourselves a table. A gentleman approached with four beers, his casual dress indicating that he was a local. We thanked him for the drinks and for his generosity.

"You're Canadians, aren't you," he said.

"How did you know?"

"Who else would golf in this weather?"

Jim and Rozanne were younger than Joan and I. They were able to enjoy Waikiki's night life more than we did. We did our share of bar hopping but they had far more stamina. We all enjoyed the riotous times we had at the Hilton's Sunday afternoon New Orleans's style jazz sessions.

After our sixth trip, Joan and I decided that we should do our own thing. We'd start with a couple of weeks in one of Honolulu's original hotels, the venerable and architecturally splendid, Halukalani. It was situated on the beachfront, very nice and very posh. After two weeks we'd be adventurous and visit Molokai, one of the smallest of the eight Hawaiian Islands. The first part of our holiday was wonderful, but the second part was a total blast. Our Molokai trip would provide me with enough anecdotes to last a lifetime.

Chapter Thirty-two

Our small commuter plane left Honolulu in a rainstorm. The weather was so bad over Molokai that we were unable to land on the island's small airstrip. It was a really bumpy, white-knuckle return flight to Honolulu but we survived. After overnighting in one of the hotels close to the airport and enjoying a leisurely breakfast, we made a smooth, uneventful, and unexpectedly short flight to Molokai. The size of the airport was equally unexpected. There was only a small group of buildings with a couple of cars parked alongside the single shuttle bus.

The ride from the airport provided a clue that this holiday would be different. The driver of the minibus was a big, happy, Hawaiian wahine.

"You're going to the Pau Hana?" she asked Joan and I, her only passengers.

"Yes."

"How long are you staying?"

"A week."

"A week?"

She turned to us as she repeated herself, almost taking the bus off the narrow road.

"A whole week?"

The Pau Hana Inn, on the outskirts of Kaunaka-kai, the main town on Molokai, was straight out of a Hemmingway story. A large banyan tree shaded the single story hotel's entrance. Another tree, even bigger, provided a canopy for the paved courtyard on the other side of the small foyer. A number of unoccupied wicker chairs were placed at random around a bamboo counter that served as the reception desk. There was also a dining room with perhaps a dozen tables.

Leilani, another generously endowed Hawaiian lady, greeted us with a huge smile.

"Aloha, Mr. and Mrs. Freckleton. Welcome to the Pau Hana."

Explaining that she was the manager, she gave us the keys to the first of a row of cabins that fronted the narrow beach. Using our names without enquiry signaled that we were the only guests that would be arriving today.

Our cabin was comfortably sparse with two rooms. The large one contained a bed, a couple of chairs, and a small table. The smaller room featured a shower, lavatory, and toilet. There was no phone, fridge, or kitchen facilities. We also discovered later that there was no air conditioning. Changing into our swimwear, we prepared for an ocean swim.

Joan and I both loved swimming in the Pacific Ocean. The invigorating cold salt water, the unpredictable waves and undercurrents that swept us off our feet, the feeling of excitement as the next big wave came rolling in. When swimming off Waikiki, each day at the beach would start with a fast swim out to the reef, then quickly back to safer, shallower water. We found the ocean easier to swim in than our swimming pool back in

Calgary. The salt water made our bodies more buoyant and the invigorating cold temperature of the ocean made our activity more energetic.

Stepping out of our cabin and onto the beach, our ocean was merely yards away. The otherwise deserted beach seemed to stretch for miles on either side of us. The water was warm. That was different. As we walked further into the ocean, we were so disappointed. It wasn't getting deeper. No waves, hardly a ripple. Half a kilometer out the water was still less than knee deep. We returned to the beach. There would be no ocean swim that day. We spent the rest of the afternoon watching dozens of tiny crabs skittering up and down the ridges in the pristine golden sand.

Later, at dinner time, Leilani greeted us as we entered the dining room. She escorted us to our table then took our orders for drinks. When our dinner was served, guess who served it!

The next morning, we walked the narrow beach before breakfast. Immediately behind the strip of sand that seemed to stretch into infinity stood a row of half a dozen beachfront residences, each with a fenced yard. We soon learned why the fences were there and why they were high.

As we passed each house, a large dog would start barking and snarling from behind the fence. Pretty soon we were hearing from all the dogs. It became quiet when we were past the last of the homes. A couple of men were casting nets in the shallow water. They were some distance into the water and we greeted them with a wave. They waved in response. After a few minutes, we decided to return to the inn. Another wave from the fishermen, another cacophony from our canine friends.

Breakfast was served by a lovely, shy young Island girl. She introduced herself as Precious. Leilani sat with Joan and I while we ate. I told Leilani that we were going to rent a car and explore the Island. She asked if we had any children.

"No." We said in unison.

"Be sure to visit Kaule O Nanahoa. It's a rock near the Kalaulapa Lookout."

She then turned to Joan.

"You have to sit on it."

At the car rental counter, the young lady gave us an indication of just how small Molokai was.

"Are you sure you want the car for the whole day?"

I asked where we would find the Kaule O Nanahoa that Leilani had mentioned. The young lady laughed and gave us directions.

Chapter Thirty-three

I'd read James Michener's monumental novel *Hawaii* following one of our previous visits to the Islands. For me, visiting the Lookout at Kalaulapa would bring his epic story to life.

As we gazed down from the Lookout, I explained to Joan that the small cluster of buildings below us was home to a group of what used to be called lepers. In our enlightened era, they are now sufferers of Hansen's disease. Most of the encampment's occupants had been removed to modern facilities on Oahu. Just a small number of these sad souls remained. The buildings were on a small strip of beach surrounded by high, almost vertical cliffs.

We watched as the ocean pounded on the rocks surrounding the deserted little beach. The spray, a dazzling white, reaching up high into the cliff face then plunging down again, regrouping for another charge at the rocks.

I asked Joan to imagine what Michener had described so graphically. The sufferers of the disease were thrown from ships into the turbulent waters. The ship's crews were afraid to get too close to the rocky shore. The lepers had to find their own way to the beach if they could. When, or rather if, they reached the shore, they wouldn't be able to climb the steep cliffs. What time was left of their pitiful lives would be spent in cruel isolation.

The first of these unfortunates arrived in 1866, the last in 1969. Father Damien, a catholic missionary, started ministering there in 1873. He died of the disease in 1889. I don't know if the church ever made him a saint, but I know they should have.

We walked over to Kaule O Nanahoa, just a couple of hundred yards from the Lookout. It was a large rock, shaped similarly to a phallus. Part of its legend was that if a woman without children sat on it she would become pregnant. I bet Joan a hundred bucks that she wouldn't sit on it. She didn't take the bet.

The rest of the day was spent touring the perimeter of the island. We passed a group of Hawaiian cowboys on horseback. The paniolos were herding cattle belonging to one of the small number of ranches on Molokai. On the far side of the island was a large hotel and condominium resort. It was not yet completed and the mandatory golf course was being laid out between the resort and the ocean.

We walked through the extremely quiet and almost deserted main street of the town after returning the car to the rental agency. A notice on the door of the closed Dairy Queen read 'Sorry, No Ice Cream.' On the barber shop door, the sign read 'Closed, come back March.' Yes, Kaunakakai was very small town.

On Thursday during breakfast Leilani informed us that there would be a dance in the courtyard after dinner. We must be sure to attend. Later, while we were at dinner, Joan whispered to me.

"Don't look now, but those four lovely ladies at the table behind you aren't ladies."

Naturally I swiveled my head around. I'd never have guessed.

"How do you know?" I asked.

"Women don't hold their cigarettes like that and their make-up is just too perfect."

A short time after dinner the tables were transferred to the periphery of the courtyard. A portable bar was stationed on one side and a small stage was positioned opposite. There was plenty of room for dancing in the center of the courtyard.

After a stroll on the beach, we entered the courtyard and after selecting a table, we went to the bar. The bartender was a rather obvious and highly-strung old 'queen.'

"What can I get you darlings?" he asked, in some sort of falsetto voice.

I ordered our drinks. He told me one of the waitresses would bring them to our table. In a minute or so, one of the young transvestites Joan had spotted earlier delivered our drinks. The other members of his/her group were also waitresses.

At the start of the evening's event, another gentleman minced onto the stage. In an even higher falsetto he made an announcement, his hands fluttering in the air.

"Proceeding will now begin."

The music was provided by a group of local musicians. What they lacked in talent they compensated for with amplification.

The courtyard was beginning to fill up. All the tables were occupied, mostly by young 'ladies.' There were very few men present. Joan said she was going to visit the restroom.

"Not without me, you're not!" I exclaimed, dreading to think what would happen if I were left sitting alone.

We went back to our cabin and listened to the blaring music, never knowing and not really caring about what we were missing. The following morning at breakfast Leilani asked us how we enjoyed the dance.

"It was a bit different."

"Oh, you noticed."

As she walked away, her shaking shoulders indicated that she was having a silent chuckle.

On the last night of our not too short stay on Molokai, the clocks seem to move interminably slowly on our quaint little island. Joan turned the covers in our bed. There was an extremely large cockroach on top of the bed sheet, just sitting there. We must have disturbed his nap. Joan dispatched me to the reception desk for help.

"We have a problem. There's a large cockroach in our bed."

The night clerk simply handed me a large can of Raid,

"No problem."

We had a blast on Molokai, as did the now deceased cockroach.

Chapter Thirty-four

Our next seven or eight annual vacations on Oahu were spent in rented, self-catering apartments, such as Discovery Bay, the Ilikai Hotel Apartments, or the Ilikai Marina. We booked through an agency. They were all situated close to the beach and the lovely yacht harbor. Located a short distance from the tourist area we were able to enjoy an atmosphere that brought us a little closer to the real Hawaii.

It was on one of these earlier vacations that I experienced my first, and only, ocean yachting trip. Jack, a friend and business acquaintance from Calgary, was on the island on an extended holiday with his lovely wife, Pat. We'd both rented apartments on different floors of Discovery Bay. Before leaving Calgary, we'd arranged to meet on the evening of our arrival. We'd have dinner at the famous Wailana restaurant, a popular establishment that we were all familiar with.

After the meal, we went into the lounge for a quiet drink. Jack asked if Joan and I would enjoy a Sunday afternoon on the ocean with him and Pat.

"Yes, of course," we both replied.

We'd previously been on afternoon and sunset cruises, but never a real ocean cruise.

"Well, here's the deal," said Jack, a self-employed sales agent. "The owner of the sailboat is also the manufacturer of a well-known suntan lotion company. He wants me to sell his product in Canada."

"That's good," I said, nodding.

"You, my friend," Jack continued, "are the owner of a string of supermarkets in sunny Alberta. You're keenly interested in stocking his line of sunscreen products in your stores."

My new-found prosperity and my interest in sunscreen was news to me. I liked it.

"How many people do I employ?" I asked, in the style of George Costanza.

Jack ignored the question.

"He's invited the four of us for a sail. We'll meet him at his yacht on Sunday at noon."

Just before midday on Sunday we arrived at the high-masted yacht, a very sleek and well-maintained craft. It was moored close to the Ilikai Hotel. At noon there was no activity either on the yacht or around it. Joan and Pat, on seeing the yacht, began to have doubts. Maybe the trip wasn't such a good idea? They decided that they'd rather spend time at the pool. Jack and I, although somewhat discouraged, resolved to wait for a short while. We both understood how Hawaii time worked. They'd get here eventually. Suddenly, around 12:15, there was lots of activity. A van arrived, followed by a couple of cars. A whole boatload of young people then went aboard the yacht. Jack introduced me to his client. Thankfully, no business was discussed. I still didn't know how many people I employed in my make-believe supermarket chain.

We were invited to board the yacht and pretty soon we were casting off. I counted thirteen people, including ourselves. Some of the young people were flight attendants and others were the yacht's crew. There was also a couple of airline pilots, a university professor, and a doctor, all friends of the owner, a slightly older than middle-aged businessman who obviously enjoyed the company of younger people.

As we made our way to the harbor entrance, the young people were filling balloons with water. I soon discovered why. They steered our yacht close to another craft and pelted the vessel and its occupants with the balloons. The hilarious laughter from the assailants was returned by hurled curses from the soaked recipients.

Once in open water, with Diamond Head the only visible landmark, a long rope was thrown over the side and left to trail behind the yacht. The new sport involved jumping over the side and catching the rope as it went by. If you missed the rope, the craft turned around and picked you up. While this was going on, Jack and I were sitting at the rear of the yacht. We were looking at each other, wide-eyed and I was ready to go back to shore ASAP.

The next stunt really gave me white knuckles. The sails were dropped and the engine switched off. Everyone on board except Jack and I jumped overboard. Yes, everyone. We both noticed that two or three bikini tops were lying on the deck. After a few minutes everyone was back on board. The sails were hoisted; the bikini tops weren't. Our afternoon sail resumed relatively peacefully and Jack and I could finally exhale.

A short time later, Jack and I both caught a whiff of what the Islanders call Maui Wowie, which in Jamaica was called Ganja. We were asked if we'd care to smoke.

"No thanks," Jack and I replied, simultaneously and emphatically.

The yacht docked just before sunset and two extremely tense and obviously unworldly Canadians thankfully stepped ashore.

Chapter Thirty-five

Joan and I always enjoyed evening strolls around the beach walk that bordered the Hilton Hawaiian Village. In the later years, I'd walk and Joan would ride her rented scooter. A Hawaiian sunset as viewed from the beach in front of The Hilton's Rainbow Tower is incomparable.

We'd watch in silence, holding hands as the sun turned into a dark crimson ball close to the horizon, then swoosh, it disappeared into the ocean. Darkness comes fast in Hawaii, with no long period of twilight. It's light then it's dark. There's no in-between.

One evening, after our sunset ritual, we walked towards our apartment home. We were staying at the Ilikai apartments. Hearing Hawaiian music coming from a bar across the street from the yacht harbor, we decided that we'd check it out. We'd discovered the Charthouse. It was a lounge and an upscale restaurant. The music was being performed in the lounge by a quaintly-named duo called Dean and Dean. Joan and I found seats facing the singers. We were seated at the back of a horseshoe shaped bar. What a wonderful hour, listening to real Hawaiian music. None of that 'Tiny Bubbles' commercial stuff.

This was the first of many evenings that we'd spend in the Charthouse, listening to the music and the voices of the duo. Sometimes high pitched, sometimes soft and gentle yet always pleasurable. We had no idea what they were singing, although obviously the songs reflected their love of the Islands. Occasionally a female patron would perform a sensual interpretive dance in the small area in front of the musicians. During breaks in the

music, Joan and I had quiet conversations with the islanders, the boat owners, the occasional tourist, and the
staff.

The following year, we booked an apartment at
the Ilikai Marina. It was a nice place on the sixth floor
although a little on the small side. We had a city view
and could also look down at the tennis players on the
rooftop courts. The Charthouse was on the ground floor.

"You don't have far to crawl," Guy, our bartender and newest friend remarked as we left each evening.

Actually, we never stayed longer than a couple of
hours. Our daily routine was, breakfast, the beach, ocean
swimming, then back to the apartment for a late lunch
and a beer or two, then down to the Charthouse. We'd
also watch the sunset. After supper we'd stroll through
the Hilton Hawaiian Village or along the beach. On one
of our walks I heard a familiar voice.

"Hey Ronnie, is that you?"

It was Anne, the advertising manager of the company we both worked for in Calgary. Anne was another
good friend of ours and was with Bruce, her husband.

"Where are you staying?" Anne asked, after we
exchanged big hugs.

"The Ilikai Marina," I replied.

"Us too," said Bruce. "Let's go to our place for a
night cap."

Their place was on a higher floor on the ocean
side of the building. The view from their lanai was spectacular. Joan was pretty emphatic.

"Next year we have to be on this side."

The following morning, on our way to the beach, we studied the notice board in the lobby. It displayed notices about accommodations for rent.

"No harm in asking," I said.

We copied the phone number from a card describing an ocean view apartment on the fourteenth floor. After lunch, and a brief phone call explaining that we'd like to rent for the month of April of the following year, we met Norm Baxter in the lobby. Norm took us up to the apartment. His wife, Anne, usually looked after the apartment rentals but wasn't available. The apartment, although fully booked for that year, would be available the following April.

It was a good-sized, well-furnished apartment. A small foyer led to the spacious living room. A counter separated the well-equipped kitchen from the dining area. A large bedroom and a spotlessly clean bathroom completed the suite. The small lanai was accessed through a sliding glass door that centered two floor-to-ceiling windows. The view was spectacular. Directly below us was the yacht harbor and beyond that was the harbor entrance and the ocean. When we stepped out on to the lanai, to the right we could see Ala Moana Beach Park and the city of Honolulu. To the left was the lagoon and the Rainbow Tower of the Hilton Hawaiian Village. Further out, we could see the beach stretching all the way to Diamond Head. The apartment was superior to any that we'd rented in previous years and the rent was reasonable. We were so happy when Norm agreed to rent it to us.

Chapter Thirty-six

After returning to Calgary, we mailed our deposit. A couple of weeks later, we received a reply from Anne asking us to be sure to let her know what flight we would be on and she'd pick us up at the airport.

In early April of the following year, walking through the International Arrivals door at Honolulu Airport, we were greeted by a smiling, mature lady. Anne was holding a cardboard sign emblazoned with 'FRECK-LETON.' We introduced ourselves. She was Caucasian but she gave us a big Hawaiian hug.

On the drive from the airport, Anne explained that she and Norm had purchased the apartment for the future. When one of them popped off, to employ her words, the other would live there. At the time they were living in a lovely house in another part of the island. It would be too big for just one of them. We also learned that Norm was a retired aviator from California. Anne was from Chicago. Their son and his family lived on Maui.

At the apartment, Anne explained how the garburator and dishwasher worked. She showed us the cupboards filled with ample supplies of linens and towels.

"If there is anything else you might need, be sure to tell me," she said.

She'd even stocked the fridge with some goodies.

"Just so you don't have to rush out shopping on your first day."

As Anne left, she assured us that she trusted us to take good care of her place. We were also to phone if we had any questions and she would be taking us to the airport on our departure date. We were ecstatic. How did we manage to be so lucky? We didn't know it at the time but this would be the first of several years that we'd stay at Anne and Norm's place. It would also be the last place in which we'd live in Hawaii.

The first time we visited Hawaii we thought it was wonderful. Each succeeding year, it became more wonderful. We were doing less, relaxing more and having more fun. We went to the public beaches that the Hawaiian's visited. We enjoyed meals in places where the Islanders frequented. We avoided the tourist areas. It was even better once we became regulars at the Charthouse. Guy the bartender was a lot of fun and excellent at his job. He had the early shift. Yes, we were always there early. Joan and I would walk in and before we reached our regular seats at the bar, Guy would have our drinks ready. A burgundy for Joan, a Bud for me. After a couple of years, on the first evening of each vacation, the first drinks were on him.

"Aloha," from Guy.

"Mahalo," from Ron and Joan.

Guy was born on Oahu. He was half-Okinawan; his Dad was an American soldier during the Second World War. Bartenders usually listen yet Guy treated Joan and I as friends. He told us about his complicated love life and how much he loved his son, Brandon. A few times, before his work day started, he'd drive us into town for lunch. We visited the famous Murphy's Bar in Honolulu and a few other popular bars and restaurants that only the locals frequented.

Scott, a friendly young man born on the island, was the Charthouse bar and restaurant manager. I learned later that one of his great-grandparents was Japanese. Being interested in all things Hawaiian, I'd have loved to have known his family history.

Jerry, Guy's fellow bartender, became another friend of ours. He was Caucasian and, like Joan and I, a wannabe Islander. I'm sure he wouldn't mind if I described him as being just a little bit quirky.

Randy completed the ensemble. He was the happy-go-lucky local boy, helping out at the bar. He'd later graduate to bartender.

These were special individuals because, in all of our years living in Canada, England, Scotland, and Wales, I can't recall ever knowing any bartenders name.

We met so many interesting people sitting at the bar in the Charthouse. So many absorbing conversations. A University of Hawaii professor told us of the history connected to the Thursday night dances at Molokai's Pau Hana. I'd related our experience on the island. She told us that the legend was that in the early days the native Hawaiians worshiped pagan gods. One god on Molokai demanded sacrifices of first-born male children. The mothers therefore dressed their male offspring in female clothes to foil the god. To my shame, I couldn't resist asking a question.

"So, the transvestites that we saw at the hotel were the fruits of their ancestor's endeavors?"

Another gentleman introduced himself as a PGA Tour professional. He pretended to be miffed when I didn't recognize his name.

"Call yourself a golfer?"

Our friends were all aware of our obsession with Hawaii. We probably bored the pants off some of them. A few decided to vacation there. Joan and I were always willing to share our experiences and point them towards their best vacation ever.

"If you come, visit the Charthouse on any weekday. We're there between five and seven."

We did meet a few old friends there. We certainly met a lot of new ones.

Chapter Thirty-seven

On the last day of our 1993 vacation we met two charming young ladies from Japan, Shinobu and Yumiko. It was early afternoon and Joan and I were enjoying our final few moments on the beach. The two petite young ladies, I would guess they were in the very early twenties, had settled down on the sand immediately in front of us. Joan, noting that they'd probably arrived in Hawaii that day, suggested to me that they'd get sunburned very quickly.

Having no further need for our suntan lotion, I told the young ladies that they should use it. I didn't suggest. I insisted. They thanked us profusely in Japanese. Who doesn't know what Arigato means? They knew the English word too.

I introduced Joan and I. They mastered Ron and Joan easily although we had a little difficulty with their names. Yes, they'd just arrived and it was their first day of a very short holiday. Their English was rudimentary. Our Japanese was non-existent. We had a lot of fun trying to converse.

"Would you take us out to the reef?"

"Can you swim?"

"No,"

"Well, we're not going out to the reef."

I explained that this was our last day in Hawaii.

"We're going home to Canada at midnight."

They were both very curious about Canada. Did we live near the mountains? They'd heard of Banff. Both were avid snowboarders. Half-expecting them to have a full itinerary, I offered to buy them a beer at the Charthouse. They thought that it was a wonderful idea. I explained where the Charthouse was.

"See that building over there? The Charthouse is at street level."

Shinobu wrote down the two words 'The Charthouse' in a neat little note book. I have no idea how she'd have written them in Japanese characters. I said that we'd be there at five.

Chapter Thirty-eight

Joan and I were seated in our usual spots when our two young guests arrived. Guy, with a wink towards me, demanded to see their ID. No problem for the girls.

"What would you like to drink?"

"Beeru."

Yumiko pointed towards my half empty glass. They were comfortable sitting between us. Shinubu touched her shoulder.

"Sunburn."

Joan's prediction had been right. When Guy served the drinks, Shinubu, before attending to her own drink, proceeded to pour my beer into my glass.

"Japanese custom," she said, noting my look of puzzlement.

"Don't get used to it," Joan said to me.

Scott and Guy joined us in our corner of the bar. Lots of laughs were mixed in with confusion over the language difficulties. Scott pretended to be upset because one of the girls said that he, being only one eighth Japanese, didn't amount to much. After a while, Joan and I said that we'd be taking one last walk around the yacht harbor.

"May we come with you?" asked Yumiko.

Before we left the bar there were the mandatory photos. Guy did the honors and there were another couple of pictures at the entrance. This was followed by a very enjoyable sunset walk while the Hawaiian sun set behind the masts of the tallest yachts. It was our last sunset of that year's holiday. Shinobu and Yumiko both had cameras and everyone took turns taking pictures of the others. A little later we said our goodbyes. There were unexpected hugs. I didn't know that Japanese people hugged. What a lovely ending to another perfect vacation.

Chapter Thirty-nine

A couple of months later, the mailman delivered a parcel to our home in Calgary. Wrapped in brown paper, one side of the box was half covered in Japanese postage stamps. Imagine our excitement as we opened the box on the kitchen table. Firstly, we saw two letters, one from Shinubu, the other from Yumiko. How much they'd enjoyed their short time with us. They hoped we'd also enjoyed ourselves. They'd enlisted the help of their English teacher to write the letters.

The items in the box were symbolic of their culture. They hoped that we'd not find them to be strange. They both expressed a wish that we'd reply to their letters. Joan and I delved into the treasure. A beautiful silk shawl, another smaller silk scarf, an ornate wooden money box with Japanese characters inscribed on the lid. A key chain with a tiny glass jar filled with rice, a small red cardboard trinket box with four tiny drawers. There was a small bag of incense in one, a Japanese coin attached to a key chain in another. There was also a little notebook and a couple of pencils covered in Japanese characters, plus a beautiful book filled with pictures of temples, shrines, ornate gardens and water features. Our two young friends had visited this famous place in the recent past.

Our joy was complete when we saw the last item at the bottom of the box. It was a large photo album entitled *Memories of Hawaii*. Shinobu and Yumiko must have spent days compiling the contents and decorating the cover and pages of the album. The first pages pictorially describing the days of their vacation, along with snippets of brochures from tourist places they'd visited, such as Hilo Hattie's, the Dole Cannery, ABC Stores, the Macadamia Nut Factory. There was even a fifty-percent discount coupon from one of Waikiki's restaurants. Mundane to some eyes, these little items were a true representation of the short-stay tourist's Hawaiian experience.

Most of the album was filled with pictures reflective of our short encounter. The beach where we met, sitting at the bar in the Charthouse, various poses of all of us as we'd walked and clicked the cameras on the sidewalk of the Yacht Harbor. Another beautiful picture showed a luxury yacht in the foreground with the Ilikia Marina in the background. The last pages pictured our two young friends visiting the temples and shrines described so vividly in the other book.

Shinobu and Yumiko had given Joan and I such a precious gift. We were able to share these pictorial memories together for many years.

I wrote separate letters to Shinobu and Yumiko. I expressed our gratitude for their wonderful and very thoughtful gifts. Joan and I were so lucky to have met them. I knew their teacher would help them read my letters but I still kept the wording simple. I wrote some details about our everyday life. I promised them that we would send some gifts to them, items that would be souvenirs of Canada.

Within a couple of days, I mailed a small package to Japan. Joan and I had enjoyed searching for things that we thought would be of interest to our two young friends. We had to be sure that we packed two of each item. Calendars complete with twelve stunning pictures of our spectacular Rocky Mountains. Canadian flags, key chains, tee shirts with maple leaves, some travel brochures featuring Banff, the Tyrell Museum at Drumheller, and the famous Calgary Stampede, two cute little Mountie dolls in their red serge uniforms. We also enclosed some random pictures of Joan and I in and around our home.

Some weeks later we received a letter from Shinobu. They were both happy to hear from us again. It was another well-structured letter with exquisite penmanship and effusive thanks for our eclectic gift package. The three-page letter ended with the comment that they would, one day, visit us in Canada. Both of our friends signed their names in English and Japanese.

Sadly, as with most holiday friendships, our correspondence became desultory and eventually we lost contact. One day, I'll search the internet and find these two lovely young ladies.

Chapter forty

In 1996, the year of our fortieth wedding anniversary, Joan's sister Maureen and her husband, Bill, visited with us in Hawaii for a couple of weeks. There was lots of room in the apartment and the sofa converted to a bed. As an ex-seafarer, Bill was in his proper element sitting at the bar in the Charthouse.

"Why don't they open at lunchtime?"

On their first evening with us, Bill and Maureen were treated to Dean and Dean singing and playing a wonderful rendition of the Hawaiian Wedding Song. The duo dedicated the song to Joan and I. At the end of the set, they joined us at the bar. Our guests were suitably impressed while Joan and I had another precious memory.

Bill and Maureen enjoyed their stay. They'd travelled from England and we made sure that they got their money's worth. We did all of the touristy things once again. Maureen couldn't swim but she just loved playing in the ocean. I think they were ready for a rest when their vacation ended. We stayed a couple of weeks longer to recuperate.

Sadly, late in the following year, our beloved brother-in-law, Bill, died after a massive heart attack at his home in St Helens.

Our 2001 vacation was the last time we'd see of our island paradise. In October of that year Joan's gastric problems necessitated major surgery. She also had a knee replacement in March of the following year.

After spending all those wonderful weeks through all of those years, we were very sad that we'd miss our Hawaii and all our friends in the Charthouse. Yet we'd always have our memories.

It was on one of our earlier Hawaiian vacations that Joan had the first of many health issues that would plague her through the rest of her days. She was admitted to the Kaiser Medical Centre with severe abdominal pain. After two days, the pain had lessened but the doctors hadn't been able to diagnose the problem. They thought it might have been food poisoning.

We returned to Calgary where our family physician could monitor Joan's health. It was on one of the monitoring visits that it was discovered that Joan had high blood pressure. The doctor prescribed daily medication to control her condition.

Chapter Forty-one

I think it was in 1978 when Marj and Stan decided to divest themselves of The Olde Pipe Shoppe. Both of their stores were successful. Consequently, they weren't getting enough quality time to spend with their special needs son, Ken. It made good business sense to sell one of the stores and concentrate their efforts on the gift store. Joan was given the opportunity to work evenings and weekends but opted not to. We'd have less free time together. Joan left the shop on good terms and we remained close friends with Marj and Stan.

Joan soon found employment at an office supply store as a store clerk. Within a year she was managing a small store in the same complex in the Calgary Tower building. A couple of years later, she was the manager of the company's flagship store in Calgary's city center.

In October 1979, we moved out of our mobile home and purchased a bungalow in the Acadia area of South Central Calgary. Our new home, built in the early sixties, was closer to my workplace. John and Lil had moved a little earlier. They bought a nice house in Ranchlands. Jim and Rozanne moved to Edgemont around the same time. I guess we all needed to build some bricks and mortar equity. We still got together, sometimes for golf, sometimes to celebrate special occasions.

Joan used to organize my annual 'surprise' birthday party. It was an opportunity for a reunion of our mobile home park group. In some years, Joan and I entertained ten or twelve of our Cascade Park friends. We had fun times, mostly reminiscing about the earlier fun times we'd all shared.

Earlier in 1979 Joan had undergone arthroscopic surgery. She'd injured her knee falling from her bike when she was a pre-teen. It was thought that the procedure would alleviate the worsening pain Joan had been experiencing. It didn't.

A year or so later, Joan was diagnosed with osteoarthritis in both knees. She had to quit the job she loved. Replacing the knees wasn't an option. The thinking at that time was that Joan was too young for the procedure. The artificial knee would deteriorate and be difficult to replace after ten to fifteen years. Today, medical professionals tend to recommend replacing the knee as soon as necessary, reasoning that the patient will have a better quality of life while they're still young.

Our lovely home was close to the local swimming pool. Joan's earlier swimming lessons gave her the confidence to join an aquazice class. The class, plus some lap swimming, helped to lessen the pain of her arthritis. I usually swam or exercised while Joan enjoyed the company of her many new friends in the class.

Chapter Forty-two

In the summer months, I golfed a couple of times each week at Canmore. Joan sometimes accompanied me on the course, riding a golf cart. On other occasions she'd stay at the trailer or visit with friends in the park. All of these activities meant that Joan was, except for the osteo-arthritis, in good physical condition to withstand the many surgical procedures that she'd be subjected to in later years.

In the same time period, I was advancing my career at the Cash and Carry. We were a division of an independent grocery wholesale company. I was promoted to assistant manager. Later, when my boss, Bill Hall, became company executive vice-president, I took over as store manager.

I really loved my job. The diversity of our customer base was fascinating. Lots of Hutterites travelled great distances from their communities, which were called colonies. These were scattered across Southern Alberta and the Hutterites spent a big proportion of their funds at our store. One of the elders explained to me that their loyalty was because of the respectful way I communicated with their people. Of course, I always had a 'good deal,' just for them.

We supplied the film crews that made the epic Superman movies. That was fun, a couple of times, I made the excuse that I had to deliver some of their needs just to get a glimpse of the stars of the movie.

Most of the mom and pop stores in the city purchased their supplies from us. I developed business associations with the various ethnic groups that our loyal customers belonged to.

Joan and I were delighted to be invited to the Korean Business Association's first Christmas party. I had helped get their association started earlier in the same year. We were the only Caucasians at the party. Paul Choi, the association president informed me that as an honored guest, I was required to sing. I reluctantly agreed with the proviso that he sing along with me. Our rendition of "Red River Valley" was somewhat pathetic but received with enthusiasm from a very sympathetic audience.

A lot of country store owners also patronized our Cash and Carry. We had everything that they needed.

I doubt that there was any segment of Calgary's business community that didn't shop at our huge wholesale convenience store at some time or another.

I was asked, many times, if I was the store owner.

"No," I always replied. "I just manage the store as though I was."

Joan and I had a lot of fun every year at my company's four-day, annual convention. It was always held at Fairmount Hot Springs on the BC side of the border. Golfing, socializing, dining, and dancing with fellow management staff, suppliers, and customers was good for business and a most enjoyable way to make good friends.

As part of the accepted way of doing business at the time, I was often invited to events, conventions, and sporting occasions by suppliers of products that we sold.

Through the years, I visited Jamaica, the Bahamas, Vegas, and Florida. These were all long weekend conventions sponsored by a national food manufacturer. I was usually accompanied by another member of our company's upper management team. Sometimes it was a favored customer that accompanied me. Unfortunately, Joan, not being a company employee, was never permitted to be part of those weekends.

Business lunches were another regular occurrence for me. Supplier's representatives, wishing to have the opportunity to establish a good business relationship, often invited me to lunch with them. I refused the majority of requests.

My all-female office staff always enjoyed teasing me, pointing out that I seemed to have lots of time for lunch with the salesladies but hardly any for the salesmen. The terms arm candy and eye candy were not in vogue at that time, but that's where my thinking was. A big boost for the ego of the shy guy who still blushes when he's teased.

Joan always knew that I'd never succumb to any temptations. I never crossed the line. I had the reputation of being a perfect gentleman. I never came close to sullying my image. My social intercourse with business acquaintances never resulted in favorable treatment. If a product was good, I bought it, regardless of who was selling it. My ethics were never questioned.

After Bill Hall retired, I was asked to join the Executive of the company. My new business card read,

Managing Director of the Cash and Carry Division. Although the title was rather grand, it did more for our bank account than it did for my job satisfaction. The tiresome weekly meetings were taking me from my real work of managing the store. My new responsibilities also lessened my interactions with my staff and our customers, the part of my job that I loved.

Chapter Forty-three

In 1987 I decided that I should start my own marketing company. I wrote out a business plan while sitting on the beach at Waikiki. It wasn't an epiphany, just something I'd often dreamed of doing.

After discussing my plan with Joan, I convinced her that we could live comfortably on our savings, pensions, and investments, even if the profits from my new venture were minimal. Another good selling point was that I'd be able to spend more time at home and with her.

I looked for opportunities and I found them. One was a signed contract to sell Olympic logo products for one of the licensees of the 1988 Olympic Games in Calgary.

I registered my company name in late 1986 and formally met with the president of the Wholesale in early December, my resignation letter in hand. My letter proposed that I'd leave the Cash and Carry in late February. The prolonged notice would give the company the opportunity to find a suitable replacement. I was flattered when the president asked that I take a lead role in the search. He agreed not to make any announcement of my pending resignation until after the New Year. We didn't need to have our staff unduly concerned about future changes in management over the Christmas trading period.

Calling in the staff that weren't on duty, I announced my pending retirement on the day after New

Year's Day. Nothing dramatic, I explained that I needed to spend more time with Joan and that my work at the Cash and Carry was demanding too much of my time. Without going into details, I told them that I planned to start my own business. I alleviated some of their concerns about their own future. My boss and I would ensure that the new manager wouldn't be making any staff changes. Why break up a winning team?

"It's okay," I told everyone. "You're just getting a new captain."

As you can imagine, the second day of January was not an ordinary day at the Cash and Carry and productivity was down to a minimum. That was okay. It was the slowest business day of the year.

Chapter Forty-four

An extremely traumatic event happened on the second Monday morning in January. Following my usual routine, I arrived at the store just a few minutes prior to our opening time of 7:30 am. Most of my staff arrived at the same time.

Our offices were situated on an L shaped mezzanine above the front of the store. My office was on the end of the long leg of the L. The stairs led up to the middle of the L. The office staff's usual routine was that they took the previous day's receipts out of the safe after I'd opened it. They'd then take the cash bags into the small office at the end of the short leg of the L.

On this particular morning, as I sat at my desk, I heard a male voice shouting in the outer office. Hurrying down the short passage, I saw a masked gunman. He was demanding that my clerk give him the bags she'd just taken from the safe. The contents of the bags were the proceeds of the previous weekend's business. My momentum had taken me to the top of the stairs and I was inadvertently blocking the robber's exit. I later guessed that he saw me as a threat to his escape. He fired a shot in my direction from his small handgun. The noise in the confined space was sharp, loud, and scary. I still remember the acrid smell of the cordite. I immediately put my hands in the air. The robber yelled at me to precede him down the stairs. Close to the bottom of the stairs, another masked man was waving a handgun at the cashiers, shouting instructions to customers and staff that they should remain still. With warnings that we shouldn't chase after them, the two men escaped in a car. It was waiting immediately outside of the front door, where a third man, the driver, was ready to make a quick getaway. It was obviously a well-planned operation.

The preceding few minutes had been traumatic, but the next few minutes contained a series of unbelievably fortuitous events that lead to the capture of the gunmen and the recovery of our cash bags. As the first gunman followed me down the stairs, Bonnie, my senior clerk, unseen in her small office, was phoning 911. With incredible luck, a police car was parked directly on the street opposite the store. The officers were ticketing a speedster.

I rushed out of the store as the culprit's car pulled away. Wayne, one of my grocery clerks, was a couple of minutes late arriving at work. Pointing at the disappearing car, I yelled at him to sprint over to the police car and tell them that we'd just been robbed. By then the police car's radio was relaying the content of Bonnie's 911 call.

" That's them," yelled Wayne, as he reached the police car.

"Jump in," said one of the officers.

The police car was now in hot pursuit of the miscreants.

My staff and I were all shaken by our taxing experience, but we soon recovered. A mixture of excitement and relief replaced fear and anxiety. I phoned to report the events to our company president and within minutes he was visiting with the staff, commending them on their actions. He demonstrated a wonderful knowledge of leadership and management skills.

Calling Joan was my next priority. One of the local radio stations was reporting that there had been a robbery in our area. I assured her that everyone at the Cash
and Carry was okay. Actually, a little later, when we examined the bullet lodged into the wooden front of our reception counter, it was less than twelve inches from
where my groin area had been when the shot was fired. I
was, indeed, a lucky guy.

A little more than an hour after we had opened
the store, Wayne arrived back at the Cash and Carry. The
culprits had been apprehended and our cash bags recovered intact. Wayne took great delight in relating the story
of his grand adventure.

He was sitting in the back seat of the police car,
its lights flashing and siren blaring as it chased the flee-
ing vehicle through our industrial area and into the rush-
hour traffic making its way into the downtown core. Red
traffic lights were ignored as both vehicles crisscrossed
the arterial roads and adjoining side streets. Finally,
heading north on McLeod Trail, after a fifteen-minute
chase, the would-be robber's vehicle, closely followed
by the police car, pulled into a blind alley next to a small
strip of shops. A branch of Country Style Donuts was situated on the end of the strip.

You've guessed it. A good percentage of the coffee shop's customers were cops, loading their carbs and
caffeine before heading to Police Headquarters to start
their workday. They had a bird's eye view of what the
TV cop shows call a classic take-down. One of the
would-be robbers tried to hide beneath the getaway car.
The other two were apprehended hiding behind parked
vehicles.

Inspector Terry Coleman, the founder of Calgary
Crime Stoppers, called me later in the day. He was one

of the patrons at the coffee shop at the time of the incident. I'd met Terry and his wife in the Cash and Carry a few years earlier. He was a Staff Sargent at the time. They were both born in Liverpool, my home town. I used to tell Terry of the different, sometimes bizarre, methods that shoplifters used to steal from our store. We apprehended a good number but I'm sure we didn't catch them all. Terry used my experiences in his many presentations on the value of crime prevention. He later became Police Chief of Moose Jaw. Later still, Terry gained great respect for his work as Chairman of various boards and committees dealing with the subject of law enforcement.

A couple of days later, I was in my office making a statement to one of the investigating detectives.

"Did someone try to deliver pizza to your home last week?"

"Yes," I replied.

Just after suppertime, on the previous Tuesday, Joan and I were relaxing downstairs. There was a loud banging on the back door. I switched on the back porch light. Through the kitchen window, I could see a scruffy individual holding a pizza box and a two-liter cola.

"Pizza."

"We didn't order pizza," I replied.

"I must have copied the address wrong. Can I use your phone?"

"No, you can't," I said.

Those words probably saved me from a lifetime of grief. Had the 'Pizza man' delivered to the front door and rang the doorbell, I'd have probably opened the door.

The detective related to me that an informant had told them that I was followed home from my workplace. The robbers intended to invade our home and hold Joan as a hostage. I was to be taken to the Cash and Carry to affect entry and open the office safe. I wasn't told what was supposed to happen to us after the robbery. I really didn't want to know. The robbery at the store was Plan B.

In retrospect, I was doubly fortunate that the robbery was foiled. Had the original plan worked, there would always be the suspicion of collusion. I was about to resign from the company. I never told Joan about Plan A. She would have spent the rest of her life in fear of the door bell ringing.

Chapter Forty-five

I named my new company, Malmesbury Marketing (Canada) Ltd. The name was from the street where I was born in Liverpool. It was also the name of a lovely little market town in Wiltshire. Joan and I used to visit there when we were at Beachley.

My immediate business plan was to market the 1988 Olympic products. For the long term, I'd develop a wholesale delivery service for penny candy. Penny candy is trade terminology for children's candy of any price. I would develop a niche, supplying candy to corner stores and specialist candy stores. In the UK we called them sweet shops.

I leased a three-quarter-ton van, added shelves and there it was, a mobile wholesaler. One of the rooms in the basement became my warehouse. I built the business to its full potential. It was profitable and it was fun. I could have expanded the business and hired staff, but that would have taken away the fun.

After the Olympics, I thought that I should continue selling logoed products. It seemed to be a lucrative market and it was.

Five years later, I disposed of the labor-intensive, candy side of the business and concentrated on golf-related logoed products.

My specialty was golf putters with corporate logos or personal names incorporated into the back of the putter head. Building each putter from scratch, I purchased the heads from Texas, the shafts from BC, and the grips from California. A local print shop helped me with the logo inserts. Now I was really having fun. My one-time basement candy warehouse was now my golf club manufacturing facility. Joan was suitably impressed.

"Don't you dare track any of that dust into my kitchen."

Selling my golf putters was never a problem. I sold a high quality product. My pricing was low because I didn't need a huge mark-up and my overheads were minimal. Best of all, the cordial relations that I always had with the manufacturer's representatives calling at the Cash and Carry paid off. Most of my early sales were to the food industry. My self-esteem took a quantum leap when I secured two orders, each for six hundred putters. The fact that I was actually manufacturing the putters with my own hands gave me a huge sense of achievement.

Chapter Forty-six

Towards the end of 1999, I decided that I'd dissolve Malmesbury Marketing. It had been a profitable experience for me, both financially and personally. I'd been able to live my dream of owning my own business and calling my own shots. Joan and I were at retirement age and we thought it proper that we should now enjoy our golden years together.

Unfortunately, it was not to be. Joan's arthritic condition was rapidly becoming acute. We purchased a mobility scooter when Joan's walking became progressively more difficult. She just loved her new candy apple red scooter. Donna, one of Joan's close friends at the aquazice class, thought it should have a name. For no particular reason the scooter was named Fred. Joan was now truly mobile, no more painful hobbling around with her walking cane. She travelled everywhere on her beloved Fred. To the pool, the malls and all around the neighborhood. In the golfing seasons she could be seen riding around the course, giving me instructions and derisive commentary on my lack of expertise. It was all in fun, of course. My playing partners enjoyed her kibitzing as much as I did.

Fred, a godsend for Joan's mobility issues, wasn't able to alleviate the pain that Joan was experiencing with osteoarthritis. Our family doctor referred us to an orthopedic surgeon and after a consultation Joan's name was added to a long waiting list for a knee replacement.

Chapter Forty-seven

Late in the summer of 2001 Joan's abdominal discomfort had become more serious. In early October of the same year, following numerous blood tests over a period lasting two or three months, all with negative results, our doctor finally found something not quite right in the latest blood tests. His instructions to me were that I should get Joan to the hospital as soon as possible. As part of the management team at the geriatric assessment unit, he was aware that there was a bed available. He had booked it for Joan.

A somewhat comedic series of events led up Joan's hospital admission. Earlier in the day, I'd undergone a hernia repair procedure at the same hospital. I was discharged with cautionary advice.

"Go home and get some rest. No driving for three days."

Arriving home after a bumpy cab ride, I was greeted warmly by Joan. She'd been worried. After a cup of tea and a sandwich, I settled down on the couch for some quiet time. The phone rang and it was my dear niece, Sylvia. She asked how I was.

"Don't forget, if you need anything, call me."

"I'm fine, Syl."

"No, Uncle Ronnie, you need a ride, you call me."

Sylvia was born with Spina Bifida, a serious birth defect affecting the spine. Survival was usually rare after childhood. In early adulthood she contracted hepatitis through a bad blood transfusion. Sylvia was a true survivor. She battled the diseases and their consequences all of her life. Sylvia lived the way she wanted to. She drove a modified van with hand controls because her lower limbs didn't function properly. A ramp was fitted to her van for motorized wheelchair access.

The phone rang again. This time it was the doctor telling me to get Joan to hospital ASAP. Now it was my turn to call.

"Hi Syl, could you take me and Auntie Joan to the hospital?"

"I'll be with you in forty-five minutes," Sylvia immediately replied.

We arrived at the hospital admissions desk ninety minutes later. I was limping along, pushing Joan in a hospital wheelchair. Sylvia completed our group in her own motorized wheelchair.

"Hi, my name's Ron Freckleton. I was here earlier today for a hernia procedure. This is my wife, Joan. There's a bed waiting for her on Unit 401."

I then pointed to Sylvia.

"And this lady is our chauffeur."

The young Jamaican woman behind the desk nearly fell off her chair laughing.

Joan underwent eight days of prodding and poking from numerous doctors. Eventually, after X-rays, C-scans and MRI's, a mass was discovered within her gall bladder. The hospital's chief abdominal surgeon was Dr. Francis Sutherland, who was also the head of one of the University of Calgary's medical teams. He described the problem and explained about the surgical procedures that he'd perform to alleviate it. He'd remove the gall bladder, part of the liver, and the lymph nodes. He also told us of the risk factor. Joan and I were both dismayed to learn that there was less than a 40-percent chance of survival.

That evening, we hugged a lot, held hands, kissed, and told each other that everything would be fine. At 11 pm, the night nurse insisted that I leave. She was sitting on Joan's bed, holding her hand as I reluctantly left. At 8 am the following morning, I was there to see Joan transported to the Operating Room. I remember the nurse reassuring me.

"Joan's in good hands. Try not to worry."

After three hours of aimlessly wandering around a nearby shopping mall, I bought some flowers and returned to Joan's room to wait for her return. It was around noon. I tried reading one of the books I'd brought from home, Irma Bombeck's *Four of a Kind*. I kept reading the same page. My mind was somewhere else.

Shortly after 3 pm, Joan and her entourage arrived. She was awake. Joan told me that she loved the flowers. I was relieved to see her looking so well. She was heavily sedated and pain free.

Dr. Sutherland and his team had performed the surgery successfully. He later told us that the mass was cancerous. The cancer had been confined within the walls of the gall bladder and Joan could expect a full recovery. Joan spent a further eight days in hospital in convalescence mode.

The latter portion of our hospital stay was a whole lot easier for both of us. Joan was recovering and I was ecstatic that my Joanie was getting better. Joan's private room became a lot more comfortable. We'd received lots of flowers and get well cards from family and friends. The cards and flowers made a lovely tableau on the sill of the window that gave us a magnificent view of our fabulous Rockies. We had lots of visitors, both family and friends. One of Joan's Acadia Pool friends, Betsy, brought a beautiful watercolor. It was her rendition of one of my photos of Canmore's mountains that I'd previously emailed to her. Betsy, an older lady with health issues of her own, was an extremely talented artist. Her generous gift proved that she was also a wonderful friend. Always grateful for our visitor's good wishes, we were more grateful that they kept their visits short and sweet.

Joan and I were able to laugh again. One nurse complained.

"Too much fun in this room. Too many endorphins."

I spent a lot of time with Joan in the sixteen days that she was in the hospital. I wore a different Hawaiian shirt each day to amuse her and keep her cheerful. It didn't hurt that the catering staff thought that I was one of the doctors. I received a staff discount each time I visited the hospital café.

On the morning of Joan's discharge from the hospital, I persuaded one of the nurses to let me use the computer. I promised her that she'd enjoy what I put on the screen. I typed in the URL for a website that I'd created at home on the previous evening. Our electronic 'Thank you' card was an immediate success with everyone on the unit. I think it was the first time that the staff had received one. This was in a time before smart phones, iPads, Facebook, or Twitter. My effusive thanks were addressed to the doctors and staff of all of the various departments throughout the hospital. I attached a number of pictures featuring the teams that had brought my Joanie back to good health. Every picture included Joan smiling happily.

A large activities room was part of the nursing unit where Joan had been staying. She thought it would be a good idea to donate her Hammond organ since she'd recently upgraded to a larger electronic keyboard. The management gratefully accepted our offer. Later they sent us a lovely thank you card, signed by all of the staff on the unit and expressing some wonderful sentiments.

A couple of weeks after Joan was discharged from the hospital, while I was on my way to the hospital to deliver the organ, I was stopped for speeding. I explained that I needed to get to the hospital to donate an organ. I guess my Liverpool humor wasn't appreciated by everyone. The young policeman wrote the ticket and handed it to me without further comment.

Chapter Forty-eight

Joan's knee surgery had been rescheduled for six months later and was performed in the same hospital without any complications. After a five-day stay, followed by a couple of months of intensive physical therapy, Joan's new knee was performing perfectly.

There was still discomfort in Joan's other knee. Her hips were also a cause for concern. The enforced weight shifting caused by Joan's disability was aggravating her hip joints. Osteoarthritis, being what it is, was destroying Joan's hips as well as her knees. A couple of years later, the orthopedic surgeon advised us that Joan should have her hip replaced.

It was during a preliminary examination that Joan's cognitive problems surfaced. The doctor asked Joan how old she was on her next birthday.

"Eighty," she replied.

I gave her a look and she quickly corrected herself.

"Oops, I mean seventy."

It seemed like a small thing but similar little incidents had happened in recent weeks.

In April 2006, about twelve months after her hip procedure, Joan needed to have her other knee replaced. She was always a very upbeat and positive person. When she had her second knee replaced, one of the nursing staff remarked that she'd never seen a patient so eager to have surgery. Joan was also eager to recover. She was on her feet and walking within five hours of the knee replacement. As we walked past the nurse's station, Joan gave the nurses a huge grin and a thumbs up.

My "bionic" Joan was now, thanks to all of the surgical procedures and her aquatic exercises, in better shape physically. However, little lapses in memory were, ever increasingly, creeping into our lives.

Chapter Forty-nine

For the next couple of years. My Joan and I lived as we always had. At least, we tried to. Joan's condition gradually worsened and I pretended not to notice. No questions. No asking "Why, Joanie?" We hugged and cuddled more than we used to. Joan was a good hugger.

Our family and friends were now aware of Joan's dementia. I'd asked Doctor Stinton, our family doctor, about this earlier.

"Should I tell our friends?"

"No. They'll know soon enough."

He always had the right answers.

Joan had developed a code of behavior that she thought would hide her condition. She greeted everyone as though they were her special friend, even the people she was meeting for the first time. Our friends treated her as they always had, ready to laugh at Joan's repartee. Always so tactful whenever Joan 'forgot herself.' Her real self was reserved for when we were alone. That was okay, she was still my Joanie. We still swam together every second day. On the alternate days I joined in the aquazice class. Aquatic activities had become a major focal point in our daily lives some years ago. Earlier, before Joan's cognitive regression, the routine was that we swam laps together on Sundays, Tuesdays, and Thursdays, always at Inglewood. We sometimes raced. Joan's backstroke was much stronger than mine. I was so proud of her ability, remembering the time when she was learning to swim. Now she was bragging to her friends.

"I can beat him, anytime."

We always swam in the early mornings. It was a good kick-start to our day. On the alternate days, I'd take Joan to her aquazice class in Acadia. Dropping her off at the door, I'd drive to Inglewood, the pool we used for swimming, where I'd complete my thirty-minute daily lap routine. The water was warmer at Inglewood and the facility was always less crowded. I would pick Joan up on my way home. Saturday was our day off.

I remember the day after my seventieth birthday when I was able to check off a bucket list item. I swam seventy laps of the twenty-five-meter pool in less than seventy minutes. This was an achievement that Joan and I bragged about. She said that she'd do the same, only faster when she was seventy.

On my golfing days in the summer, perhaps once or twice each week, I'd drop Joan off at the pool. Her good friend, also called Joan, would drive her home. That arrangement had to come to an end when my Joan's cognitive degeneration became more pronounced. We ceased our visits to Inglewood for the same reason. I was concerned because dressing after her swim was becoming problematic. There were no issues before swimming since Joan put on her swimsuit before we left home. After each swim, she dressed quickly, obviously not showering or drying herself properly. Waiting for me in the foyer, Joan would tap on the door of the men's changing room.

"Ronnie, are you ready yet?"

I was also concerned that Joan may one day wander off, thinking that I'd already left.

I started using the exercise room at Acadia while Joan continued to enjoy the company of her very supportive friends in the aquazice class. I walked for miles on the treadmill. Joan made a point of telling her friends.

"Look there's Ronnie's behind. He's on the treadmill."

The word incorrigible is not enough to describe Joan's mischievous sense of fun.

To access the gym one walked along a passage that fronted the pool. Windows separated the passage, pool, and exercise room. Joan could see me on the treadmill while she was doing her thing. She was at ease when she could see me.

I always completed my exercises before Joan's class ended. It gave me the opportunity to shower and dress without being anxious. When I walked along the passage back to the change room, Joan and I gave each other a wave. Soon the whole class would be waving enthusiastically. One day, Joan blew me a kiss, which I returned. You've guessed it. From that day forward, as I walked to the changing room, everyone in the class, including Dara, the instructor, our long-time friend and instigator of the mass affection, were blowing kisses at me.

In later days, I joined Joan and her group of friends in the water. Joan didn't like anyone invading her space or splashing her, even accidentally. She was never polite when she communicated her displeasure. Of course, Joan's friends always minimized the outbursts.

"Okay, Joanie," said Donna. "We'll straighten things out."

My presence in the water next to Joan was a calming influence and further disruption was either avoided or short-lived.

Eventually, Joan's condition got worse. She lost her enthusiasm for aquazicing and for the social intercourse with her friends. I think I needed a break too. Six months later, with the encouragement of her best buddies, and knowing that it was necessary for us to not become isolated, we rejoined the aquacize class. I had Joanie's picture printed on one of my tee shirts, with the caption 'I'm with Joanie.' I wore it in the pool. Joan loved it.

"See my picture?"

Sadly, Joan's condition was becoming worse. Anti-social behavior and dressing room issues were becoming more pronounced. We gave up on the pool although our friends didn't give up on us. We were always invited to the coffee mornings the group held every couple of months or so. Joan never wanted to attend but as soon as we arrived, she switched on. Everyone in the room got one of Joan's big hugs.,

"Wasn't that lovely?" said Joan, when we left. "Shall we come back next week?"

Chapter Fifty

We continued to enjoy our retirement as best we could, with the occasional company of our friends and family and our quiet times together. The difference now was that I was more conscious of Joan's memory lapses and behavioral missteps. They were happening more frequently.

As time went by, I lessened my golfing activities and we sold our lovely trailer. I didn't want my Joan wandering off into the mountains while I was on the golf course. We didn't sell our memories. I would always have them.

Everyone has a memory of a very special time and place. Summer evenings at our Canmore mountain retreat is mine. Number one on my 'I remember' list.

Joan and I would sit, comfortable in our loungers, both chairs securely anchored to the miniscule patch of grass that fronted our holiday trailer. Perhaps we'd had a lovely day on the golf course, or we might be unwinding after a stress filled week at our respective workplaces. If our bodies and minds were sometimes induced to further relaxation by sharing a bottle of fine burgundy, that was permissible. We were grown-ups.

Our 360-degree panoramic view captured all of our majestic mountains. Whichever way we faced, they surrounded us. We sat in the best seats of the world's most picturesque amphitheater. The Royal Range to our north, each peak named for British royalty. The awesome Three Sisters to the east. The huge Rundle Range, purported to be the largest rock in North America, to the south. And of course the magnificent Cascade Mountain, her gentle southern slope pointing the way down to the township of Banff, was to our west.

The contented hours always began in the late afternoons or early evenings. We didn't call them happy hours since to do so would invoke visions of boisterous frivolity. We were there to appreciate the natural beauty around us. Some would call it peaceful meditation. There was never much conversation as this was a place of tranquility.

Sitting with our backs to the setting sun, we'd marvel at the changing hues as the sun's rays highlighted a particular buttress close to the top of our favorite, Ha Ling's Peak. It was the closest mountain to our vantage point.

In 1896, a Chinese cook employed by Canadian Pacific Railway had made the difficult climb to the mountain's summit to win a $50 bet. After that momentous achievement, the mountain was named Chinaman's Peak. Predictably, the sensibilities of modern thinking brought a new name. That didn't concern Joan and I. We loved our mountain, whatever it was called.

Once, as a game, Joan and I took turns relating our very differently imagined recollections of the famed Ha Ling. Joan described him as a young man with a wife and a baby girl. Forced to leave them behind in a rural area of China, he'd vowed to save enough money to reunite his family. His epic climb and the resultant financial windfall would enable him to reach his goal.

Joan warmed to the story she told of the hardships and heartbreak the couple had endured, before their joyous reunion at Vancouver's busy dockside.

I asked if it were possible that future generations of this family would become pillars of our Canadian society.

"Of course," Joan replied.

She was right. We had real life friends with family histories that proved her point.

My extremely short yarn couldn't match Joan's love story. I told of a man willing to risk his life to win a bet. If he succeeded, the money would pay off his gambling debts. His inept card playing had landed him between a rock and a hard place, so he chose to climb the rock.

Yes, our Canmore days are gone, yet our priceless memories will be with me forever.

Chapter Fifty-one

I caught the gardening bug when I retreated from golf. It was something to do as I watched over Joan. Wayne Smith, the retired president of the company that I used to work for, was the catalyst. He was an avid gardener, growing the finest dahlias. We'd become friends after he retired and became Chairman of the Board. I was the manager of the Cash and Carry, which was a division of a large independent food wholesale company. Wayne would phone me at work.

"Ron, are you busy?"

"Yes, sort of."

"I've got a tee time for eleven o'clock. Do you think you could make it?"

Who was I to refuse a request from the Chairman of the Board? Off the golf course it would be Mr. Smith. On the golf course it was Wayne. One day the new president of the company called me.

"Are you golfing with Mr. Smith tomorrow?"

"No."

"Good, I can call an executive meeting."

I just hoped he was joking.

After I left the company, Wayne and I remained close friends. Joan and I loved to visit his fabulous garden. His dear wife Ethel would invite us into the gazebo for some iced tea or lemonade. She was such a sweet, generous lady. One day, Wayne was in the process of giving me some excess dahlia tubers and gladioli bulbs.

"Joan would like two of those geraniums too," Ethel remarked, although Joan hadn't said anything.

"Of course dear," Wayne replied, as he handed me two beautiful Martha Washington's. He told me later that he'd just purchased them from the local garden center. He loved his Ethel as I loved my Joan.

Wayne fired my passion for gardening by supplying me with his excess plants. I'd convinced him to purchase a computer shortly before his eightieth birthday. This resulted in lots of phone calls,

"Ron, my screen's gone blue."

"Ron, how do I send an email?"

He caught on quickly. My consultant's fees were dahlia tubers.

Without realizing it at the time, gardening became an ideal diversion for me. I was able to spend lots of quality time in the garden, knowing that Joan was watching me instead of me watching her. She was happy to sit and supervise. My enthusiasm grew as our garden took more of my time.

Wayne's dahlia tubers never failed to produce wonderful flowers, some as big as dinner plates. At the end of my second year of gardening, I learned how to lift and store the dahlia tubers. Each succeeding year, I was able to plant a lot more flowers. Wayne's dahlia tubers were the gift that kept on giving.

The first year I planted tomatoes I had beginner's luck. The resultant bumper crop meant that, for a while, none of our visiting friends went home without a bowl of the delicious fruit. They all thought I was some kind of gardening genius but I knew better. It was just plain luck.

Call it divine providence or a fortunate coincidence, but a year or so before Joan's cognitive degeneration surfaced, we had a sunroom attached to the den. It would later become our sanctuary. Joan would sit in 'her' chair watching me pottering in the garden.

"You missed a bit!" she'd say as I was mowing the lawn.

"Time to come in," she'd remark when she got restless.

I took great pride in 'Joan's' garden. It seems that I had a green thumb that I never knew about. I redesigned and enlarged the borders. The lawn now took on a sculptured look. No longer rectangular, it flowed around the L-shaped area, making the garden appear so much bigger.

The large apple tree, close to the fence, was ideally placed directly in front of the sunroom. Joan could watch the activities of the various birds that chose to share our peaceful garden. Robins often nested in the higher branches of the tree. Their 4 am wake-up calls were welcome although I was already awake. Joan and I enjoyed watching them bathing and drinking from the bird bath or foraging in the lawn or borders. The sight of mom or dad robin with a beak full of worms always delighted Joan. Each time we saw them was a new experience for her. Her lack of short-term memory ensured that.

I took lots of pictures in our colorful garden. Joan loved to pose. Sometimes with her face close to the large blooms, sometimes embracing a large bunch of freshly picked flowers. With a digital camera, there was no limit to the number of pictures I took. Each year I chose the best two, had them enlarged, then printed onto a foam backing and laminated. These Christmas stocking stuffers eventually became our pictorial gallery on the transoms above our sunroom windows. Every winter, the pictures of our beautiful flowers reminded Joan and I that summer would return.

My gardening took a couple of even more ambitious turns. I built a seed propagation and seedling growing unit in the basement. It was very basic. A set of four feet shelves, each with a pair of florescent tubes above. Our basement was now my indoor gardening facility. My summertime gardening had morphed into a year round hobby. I was able to start a variety of flower and tomato seeds in January. Yes, my basement was now 'a grow op' although I wasn't tempted to grow any illegal stuff.

The result of my basement activity was an abundance of plants. They would be ready to transform the nondescript frozen ground of winter into a blaze of spring color just as soon as the last frost disappeared. Geraniums became another yearly garden feature. My first attempt at starting them from seed produced a 98-percent success rate. Joan was as impressed as I was. Scarlet red geraniums would now cover the fronts of all the flower borders, just behind the vibrant blue lobelia.

I also purchased a large greenhouse that fitted nicely on the South facing deck. In early May it would bulge with a large variety of plants that I'd transferred from the basement. Of course there was always extras. Family and friends helped me eliminate the surplus.

Chapter Fifty-two

Joan and I spent long summer afternoons sitting on our favorite chairs in the sunroom, enjoying our beautiful garden. As the kids would say, we were 'just chilling.' A couple of beers for me, for Joan, a glass or two of burgundy. Each afternoon I'd talk of the lovely memories that I hoped we shared. I'd relate one particular event from the past, gauging from her feedback if she was remembering too. Sometimes she'd remember, at other times she pretended that she did. Those poignant days hold memories for me that will last forever.

In the cooler days and in the winter we'd sit in the living room. Joan sat at her keyboard while I listened quietly on the sofa.

I bought Joan her first piano, actually it was a small Hammond organ, in December 1975. She just loved it. It was the best Christmas present ever. I hadn't known that she could play piano until she'd surprised me a couple of weeks earlier. She couldn't read sheet music and played by instinct. I called it playing by ear. If she heard a tune once, she could play it. I never heard her play ragtime, jazz, or fast paced music of any genre. Joan loved ballad-type show tunes. She adored The Beatles, our hometown heroes. She'd play for an hour or two, just for her own enjoyment. Before her dementia, never, and I mean never, would she play for friends or guests.

I bought a Yamaha key board when we moved into our Acadia home. The Hammond went down to the basement. We later donated it to the hospital. Later still we purchased a bigger and better Yamaha. The first one we moved into our Canmore holiday trailer. She shall have music wherever she goes.

Joan continued playing her keyboards well into the years of her dementia. The only difference was that now she'd play in anybody's presence. Friends and family could listen in wonder at my Joanie's talent, hidden for so long. She had a set repertoire. George Harrison's *Something*, The Beatles *Yesterday*, *Memory*, from *Cats*, *The Way We Were*, *Don't Cry for Me Argentina*, Ringo's *Yellow Submarine*. After the 1988 Olympics she added Beethoven's *Ode to Joy* to her list of favorites. We always knew her recital was coming to a close when she played *Someone to Watch Over Me*. Yes, she knew she had dementia and she knew that she had me to watch over her

The latest keyboard had a recording component. Joan had recorded some of her rendering when she was in the early stages of dementia. Her musical talent will never be erased and will always bring her into my presence at the touch of a button.

Chapter Fifty-three

Cognitive degeneration was a phrase that I'd use often. If Joan said or did something inappropriate, I never corrected her. I excused her by quietly telling the person that Joan had cognitive degeneration. Joan was unconcerned when I used that terminology, whereas had I said Joan has dementia, I'm sure we'd have a meltdown on our hands.

Dementia had taken my old Joan and left me with a new Joan, one that needed me more. I loved the new Joan as I loved the old Joan. I always would. 'In sickness and in health,' was part of the marriage vows that I'd taken. I don't break vows nor do I want to. I made a new vow. I'd keep my Joan as happy as I possibly could, for as long as I could.

Joan and I spent more quality time together in the years of our dementia struggles than we ever did in the glory days of our long and happy marriage.

I researched the internet looking for clues on how to deal with dementia. I soon realized that I wouldn't benefit from anything gleaned from that source.

I read Michaelle Jean's essay, *The Insidious Fog*. She elegantly described her mother's struggles with dementia. Michaelle was the Governor General of Canada. The disease was indiscriminate. I thought her purple prose gentrified the disease. There is nothing gentle about dementia.

I also saw the harrowing movie, *Iris.* This was the story of Iris Murdoch, an academic and novelist born in Ireland and educated in England. The original biography was written by John Bayley, her husband. Dame Judy Dench, acting the part of Iris in her later years, after she fell prey to dementia, brought a chillingly realistic performance to my TV screen. The scenes as the disease gradually took hold of Iris, gave me a horrifying insight into our own future. The squalor and filth of the home in the closing scenes as Iris was carried into an ambulance, terrified me. Please God, don't let that happen to me.

Chapter Fifty-four

Dr. Don Stinton became my mentor. He'd been our GP for more than a quarter of a century. Dr. Don's special interests were care of the elderly and delivering babies. Who wouldn't put their trust in someone with those priorities? He advised me on how to act in given situations in just four words.

"Go with the flow."

He also advised me against confrontations.

"Joan will forget them in a minute, you will not. It's okay to make promises you can't keep. Little white lies are okay too."

As long as Joan was content, that was his message. Whatever it takes, keep Joan happy. He told me what to expect in the future months. He also appraised me of Alberta's health system and how things would unfold as Joan's affliction worsened.

I wasn't a saint. In the early days I sometimes let my frustrations bubble to the surface. I quickly learned that if I got angry, Joan got angry too.

One of the first symptoms was repetition. Joan would ask a question, I would answer. A couple of minutes later, the same question, the same answer. This could go on for a while. Joan was just forgetting that she'd already asked. After the first few times, when I told her that she'd already asked, I realized that it would be so much easier for both of us if I simply answered each time she asked. Pretty soon it was a game for me but serious conversation for my Joanie.

Another symptom then emerged. Joan was forgetting how to cook. She'd never allowed me to interfere in her kitchen. She always resented my advice when I tried to help her.

"What do you know about cooking? You're a man."

She thought that she was hiding her memory impediment by purchasing convenience foods. No complications, just pop them in the microwave but she couldn't do that with everything. There were times when we were eating some, shall we say, interestingly different meals. I never complained or even commented. It would have been totally counterproductive. Of course, burned saucepans and the resultant messy stovetops are common occurrences associated with early onset dementia. I cleaned up without audible comment. Joan's lack of short-term memory always meant that the latest mishap was quickly forgotten.

"Who made this mess? Are you going to clean it up?"

Eventually it was agreed that I would 'help' in the kitchen and dietary order was restored. No more scraping the congealed spaghetti off the bottom of the dish. No more really creamed potatoes that were supposed to be mashed. God bless my Joanie, she'd tried so hard.

We kept to a regular meals schedule. Breakfast at 8 am after I'd helped Joan wash and dress. Lunch at noon and supper at 5 pm. I found it easier to serve Joan her lunch in the den. She had her favorite rocking chair, her TV, and a small table close at hand. Lunch was not extravagant. A filled bread roll or a sandwich, plus a peeled and sliced apple.

Joan's memory loss was evident each lunchtime. She'd forget that she'd eaten. Around 1 pm she'd ask when lunch was. She never believed me when I told her that we'd already had lunch even though the empty crockery was still on her table. A little later, she'd sneak into the kitchen and prepare another lunch, including her peeled apple. I let her get on with it. What difference did it make? I solved the problem by serving half of her lunch at 12 and the other half an hour or so later. Some dementia sufferers just forget to eat. My Joanie was the opposite.

Personal hygiene was extremely problematic. It was difficult for me to balance the need for cleanliness and the knowledge that Joan should preserve her dignity. Joan had always been a modest and very private person some would say even prudish. Cleanliness won out. Any loss of dignity would be short-lived. Joan's memory loss would ensure that. Undressing her wasn't the fun it used to be.

My descriptions of our bathroom battles will not be all encompassing. I have no desire to make public all of Joan's indignities. As dementia progressed, Joan went from a daily shower to twice-weekly then once each week.

After supper my routine consisted of getting Joan to the downstairs bathroom where the walk-in shower was located. I didn't tell her the plan. If I had, I'd never have been able to get her down the stairs.

Joan and I would have a wrestling match to get her undressed.

"What are you doing? Wait 'til I tell our George. He'll beat you up."

Assuring Joan that it wouldn't take long, I'd set the water at a comfortable temperature. I would usher, well maybe I mean push, Joan into the shower enclosure. We had a hand shower attachment, which was invaluable. My attempts to get all of Joan showered often lead to Joan grabbing the shower head and turning the shower on me. I pretended that I was having fun. I wished I was. Once we started the shampooing process, Joan would usually become cooperative and we'd proceed without any further complications.

"Doesn't it feel good to be so nice and clean?"

"Yes, lovely," she'd say.

After each shower, I redressed Joan in her night clothes. She was ready for bed whenever she chose to retire. Another battle was over and we'd both won.

Sleep was a precious commodity. My normal sleep pattern disappeared. If I slept for two hours on any night I considered that to be a good night's sleep. I convinced myself that if I relaxed my body, I wouldn't be tired the following day. My mind told me that I needed to stay awake to ensure that Joan didn't wander around or out of the house. Unlike most dementia sufferers, Joan very rarely wandered around the house during the night. I think that the arthritic pain she suffered as she tried to lift herself out of the bed acted as a deterrent.

Joanie usually slept well. By this I mean that she slept for long periods. I believe her troubled mind may have caused dreams that disturbed her. I held her close when she was restless. She needed to know I was with her when she woke.

There was a period when, each morning, Joan would wake and ask me about people.

"Where's my Mam?" she'd sometimes say.

Sometimes she'd mention her dad.

"Where's my Dad?"

On other occasions she was asking about her beloved elder brother George. Perhaps Joan was waking early and just lying awake, thinking of her family.

"They're back home," I always answered. "They're doing fine."

Any other answer would mean more questions.

Joan's mom died in 1977 after a courageous fight with breast cancer. Her dad passed a couple of years later of pneumonia. He never recovered from the loss of his beloved Katie and just gave up. Joan's younger brother, Jim, later told us what had happened.

"Dad went a bit funny in the end."

I think Jim was probably aware that his dad had dementia. It would have become more pronounced when Katie was no longer there, helping him hide it from the kids. Joan's lovely brother George was diagnosed with dementia in 2002. Kitty, George's childhood sweetheart and loving wife, cared for him in their home for a number of years until he became unmanageable. He was placed into a care center and in 2013 succumbed to pneumonia.

Earlier, at the start of Joan's dementia, when she mentioned her hero brother, George, she always talked of him as having a nervous breakdown. She didn't wish to use the word dementia. I guessed that she was still trying to hide her own condition, if only from herself. I always gave her a big hug. There was nothing that I needed to say.

On the day Kitty phoned me with the news of her tragic loss, I decided that I needed to pick the right moment to tell Joan of her beloved George's death. I knew I should be ready for an extreme emotional reaction from her. The moment came and I told her as gently as I could. We hugged, Joan stayed silent, no tears, but I could feel the sadness within her. I consoled her with gentle kisses and the moment passed.

Chapter Fifty-five

I still endeavored to keep our day to day activities on a normal footing. When we did our weekly grocery shopping, we went to the supermarket at the same day and time each week. I usually picked a checkout with a familiar cashier. Joan had endeared herself to most of them. Her cashier experience in the past created a bond and there was always lots of laughter as we checked out.

On one occasion, a cashier at one of the other checkouts called out to us.

"Hi Joan. Hi Ron,"

"You know," our cashier said, "all of us love you guys."

I was trying to hide my tears as I wheeled the shopping cart to the car.

On our visits to the malls, I made sure that we visited the Dollar Store. I'd give Joan a $10 or $20 bill. I'd then sit on a bench outside the store. Joan would spend a blissful half hour or so 'shopping.' It didn't matter to me what she purchased, my Joan was happy. Our pantry and cupboards were filling up with some weird stuff. Big deal.

One thing she purchased, which I didn't notice for a couple of days, was a little imitation parchment scroll. It was a declaration entitled *Accept Me*, a homily written by Larry S. Chenggies. This is how it began:

"I am I. Do not change me."

It went on for a few lines, ending with,

"I am I… and I like being what I am… Me."

Joan had signed it and hung it on the inside of one of the kitchen cupboards. I still have it. Another precious memory.

A less pleasant symptom was probably caused by Joan needing to feel secure. She became secretive and deceptive. Joan had saved what in the UK was called 'running away money', or in Canada, 'mad money.' She spent a lot of hours counting and recounting it in the privacy of the bedroom. I had no problem with this. In fact, I would occasionally add to her hoard by gifting her small amounts. I used to tease her about how rich she was.

Later, as her dementia worsened, I worried about her losing her purse. I diminished her hoard, leaving her with twenty $5 bills. Joanie never noticed the difference. Some days later we were sitting in the den and Joan was in her favorite chair, pottering with her possessions. I was working on the computer with my back to her.

"Look what I've got."

She waved her stack of fives at me. She'd doubled her money. Every bill was cut in half. I laughed, dug out my roll of scotch tape and spent the rest of the afternoon taping the bills together. Joan had shuffled the pieces. It was fun putting the right halves together. There are worse ways of spending an afternoon when your loved one has dementia.

A real concern was that Joan had taken to hiding various house and car keys. Her lack of short-term memory meant that she didn't know where she'd hidden them. There were times when we spent days looking for something precious. I rationalized her behavior as a need to feel that the house was hers. I had to resort to hiding my sets of keys to prevent any problems. An associated concern was that Joan would lock the doors when I was in the garden or in the yard. Even when I took out the garbage I'd have to coax Joan to unlock the door. Joan always claimed that she didn't mean to lock me out. I learned to always carry a set of house keys.

One difficult day, Joan told me to get out of her house.

"It's my house too," I replied, in what should have been a quiet manner, but wasn't.

"We'll see about that."

She grabbed the phone and dialed 911. Quickly realizing what she'd done, she hung up the phone. One minute later, the 911 operator called. It's standard procedure to follow up on emergency calls. I told her of the situation. Less than five minutes later, I was inviting two policemen into our home. I told them my name.

"Tell the policemen your name, Joan."

"Joan Sandison," she replied.

This had been her maiden name. They accepted my explanation. Nice guys, both expats from England. They stayed for a few minutes and Joan was amicable, putting on another show. We engaged in some small talk and after refusing my invitation of a cup of tea, they left. Joan's lack of short-term memory meant that she'd forget the incident immediately. I had to put it into my memory bank so that I could avoid any other similar occurrences. I also disconnected the kitchen phone.

Chapter Fifty-six

Joan was beginning a new phase. I suppose we can call it non-cooperation. If I wanted to dress her, she resisted. If she needed to be undressed, she fought that too.

"It's suppertime, let's go into the kitchen."

"No."

"Let's go to bed," I'd say at bedtime.

"No."

When I got her into the bedroom, she didn't want to lie down. In the mornings, she didn't want to sit up. If I tried to help her out of her chair or our bed, she'd resist. She wasn't just making herself dead weight but she would also strain in the opposite direction.

Joan fell a total of four times during her dementia. Once, she fell off a lounger onto the deck. On another occasion she fell in the bathroom and twice in the bedroom. We were fortunate that she sustained no injuries. It was difficult getting her back on her feet. The only method that worked for me was to get Joanie sitting on a blanket. I would drag the blanket over the hardwood floor in the hall and kitchen to the top of the basement stairs. Joan enjoyed the rides. I'd coax her to put her feet onto the next two steps down. With the help of the banister rail and standing below her, I was able to get Joan upright. It was heavy work for a guy in his late seventies. It really gave my hernia a workout. I learned later that I should have called the firefighters. They would lift her, no problem.

Chapter Fifty-seven

In early April 2010 Joan became ill with gastric discomfort. She became unwell and had periods of violent vomiting in the bathroom. This only happened in the late evenings. I speculated that the vomiting might be self-induced. I made an appointment to see Doctor Stinton.

On the Tuesday morning of our doctor's visit, Joan's condition had become much worse. She was lethargic, with no energy and none of the fiery resistance that I usually encountered as I dressed her. Her anemic appearance concerned the doctor. He asked me to take Joan to the medical centre in town. It was situated just a few blocks from his office. They'd be more able to assess Joan's condition, have blood tests processed more quickly, and make the proper clinical decisions.

After a three-hour anxious and frustrating waiting period, we were ushered into a small room. A further fifteen minutes were spent listening to a doctor through the thin wall that divided the next examining room from Joan's. He was explaining to his patient that her problem really was only a common cold. A different doctor, a very proficient South Asian, gave Joan a very comprehensive examination. She immediately made arrangements for Joan to be transferred, by ambulance, to one of the major hospitals in the city.

"She's very sick," she said as her closing comment to me. "The next couple of days will be crucial."

An hour later, around 4 pm, I arrived at the hospital. It was the same one that Joan had been in during her brush with cancer just a few years earlier. I was directed to one of the waiting areas in the Emergency Department. This waiting area was a wide corridor through which ambulance personnel wheeled their patients into the emergency rooms. Today, the corridor was lined on both sides with ambulance gurneys. Each one had an occupant and was attended by two ambulance personnel. It was a regulation that ambulance personnel were to care for their charges until hospital staff became available.

I found Joan with her two Samaritans by her side. She'd been triaged and was waiting her turn. Quiet and alert, Joan was glad to see me but I was concerned. If she'd been triaged, why wasn't she in one of the emergency examination rooms? Our ambulance driver told me that, for some unknown reason, that afternoon all ambulances in the city had been directed to this hospital. The resultant chain reaction effect was that there were no beds available in the hospital and patients in the process of being admitted to the hospital from the Emergency Department couldn't be moved out of the ER.

I stood at Joan's side, refusing the offer of a chair. Joan needed to know I was with her. The time was passing so slowly. Joan lay on her gurney, holding my hand. I swapped stories with the paramedics. They told me how their system worked. I was disturbed to witness so much EMS expertise being wasted. These highly qualified people were detained for hours in this hospital waiting area.

The mood lightened when I related some of the anecdotes I'd gleaned from our last visit to this hospital. They particularly liked my stories about our admission experience and my organ donation excuse with the speeding ticket.

At 8 pm Joan's name was called. There were cheers from Joan's crew, groans from the other paramedics. As soon as Joan was in one of the emergency pods, a young doctor, probably an intern, examined her. He ordered immediate transfusions and an IV solution. Joan had severe anemia and she was also dehydrated. Job one was to get Joan into a stable condition. The doctor returned an hour later. There was more poking and prodding then without any warning to Joan or me, he subjected Joan to a digital, rectal exploration. He immediately apologized profusely as Joan screamed her objection to this sudden and unexpected violation to her body. With the opportunity to prepare Joan for this indignity, the experience could have been a lot easier, and quieter for all concerned. It was probably his first time. Let's hope he learned something.

Later into the night, a doctor, whom I assumed was the hospital's top gastroenterologist, pulled the curtain aside. He was lower down the list when it came to bedside manners.

"Got a little dementia, have we?"

Joan stiffened. I bristled. He proceeded to tell Joan his diagnosis and his proposed actions in great detail, including the width of the tube to be used for the colonoscopy procedure. If his purpose was to traumatize Joan, he was doing a great job.

"Of course if the issue is cancerous, we will operate without delay."

Did he miss the dementia patients have no short-term memory seminar? Did he have difficulty talking to healthy people? He never addressed any remarks to me.

Joan was to drink all of the contents of a three-liter jug to enable the intestines to be clear of impurities.

"A cold water enema, if she doesn't drink it all," he added, in a loud aside to the nurse. "No food until after the procedure."

I wondered if they were missing him back at De Sade School of Medicine. I also wondered if he'd trained the intern with the extra-large finger.

Even later into the evening, after midnight, we had a visit from a person that I believed to be the resident doctor. A young lady in her final year of Med School. She was being mentored by a practicing GP who was unable to be with her and would visit tomorrow. She studied Joan's chart intently. I wasn't paying too much attention. She left after initiating a debate with me on the meaning of the contents of our Personal Directives.

I stayed with Joan throughout the night and the next day. Her dementia heightened. She became delusional. Probably the combination of no sleep, no food, differing medications, and trauma triggered by the GE doctor's lack of tact.

"Where are the suitcases? This bed's too small for both of us."

She thought we were in Hawaii. Her ramblings turned to efforts to get out of the bed.

"I'm not staying here. Where's my coat?"

I had to call the nurse as Joan tried to tear off the IV tube attached to her arm. Later in the day there was more of the same behavior. The transfusions and medications had made Joan stronger. Her increased energy level meant that she could maintain her erratic behavior. The rails prevented her from getting out of bed. She slid her body down and got out from the bottom. She was uncooperative with the nursing staff.

My sweet Joan was uncontrollable. She was using language that I'd never heard her use before. Her voice changed and her Liverpool accent became more pronounced with a deeper timbre. I guessed that she thought that she was her brother, George. She sounded just like him.

The staff psychiatrist was called to prescribe a sedative. An hour or so later, he was recalled. Something stronger was needed. A stage six security alert was instigated. I learned that because staff members felt endangered, a security guard was to be positioned at Joan's bedside. Stage six was the highest alert.

"Leave him to me," Joan whispered to me.

"Hi, how are you?" she said to the guard, as she winked at me. "Aren't you a bit young to be a policeman."

Joan was acting as though the situation was perfectly normal. She engaged the young man in a quiet conversation. I was bemused. Was my Joan back or was she pretending? It was an act. The young man stepped outside. Joan immediately turned to me.

"Quick, get my coat, we're getting out of here."

Another epic struggle followed to get her settled down again.

As the evening turned into night, and after another visit from the psychiatrist, Joan became quieter as the latest dose of sedatives were taking effect. Around midnight, she was snoring. The charge nurse advised me to go home and try to get some rest.

I arrived home around 1 am. I was exhausted but I knew that I wouldn't sleep. I decided that a bowl of soup would help. Next I sent an email to Joan's family, my family, Lucille and Ralph, plus a couple of other close friends. I explained Joan's condition, the prognosis that I'd received, and the happenings over the previous two days. It made for pretty bleak reading. In hindsight, I shouldn't have sent the email. I was suffering from sleep deprivation and definitely not thinking straight, but I supposed that writing the email was somewhat cathartic.

I thought a 2:30 am shower would help me sleep. It did but I only slept for two hours. After another thirty minutes lying awake in bed, trying to plan my day and knowing that I had no control over what might actually happen, I resolved to do what I could for my Joanie. I'd put on a brave face, whatever the day brought us.

It was a good start. Although it was only the second week of April, six beautiful little daffodils were about to bloom in our garden. The delicate scent of these lovely flowers was exquisite. They were in the sheltered border facing south. I cut them as low down the stems as I could. Joan would love them.

As I entered Joan's ER pod at 7:30 am I was greeted by the day shift's charge nurse.

"Joan had an accident this morning. We had to change her sheets."

"Whoop de doo," I thought to myself. "She's had enough tranquilizers pumped into her to knock down an elephant and you're concerned about some soiled sheets."

Joan was sleeping so I sat quietly by her bedside. Her lovely daffs were on the bedside table in the small crystal vase I'd brought with me. One of the nurses came in. She admired the flowers and marveled that they were from our garden in Calgary.

It was time to wake Joan.

"May I wake her?"

I leaned over Joan, the vase in my hand.

"Hi Joanie. Good Morning. Smell the lovely flowers."

Joan woke up and gave me a little smile

"Good Morning. They're lovely."

This was my real Joan.

"Hi Joan," said the nurse. "Do you know where you are?"

"Yes," Joan replied.

"Where are you?"

"I'm here."

"Good answer," said the nurse, laughing.

My Joan was definitely back. The nurse beckoned me to step outside.

"Joan is booked for a colonoscopy later this morning. We'll be giving her medication. She will be conscious but won't feel any discomfort. Before then, we have to give her an enema."

"I'll help with that," I offered.

I cradled Joan's head as she lay on her side. Holding her hands, I commiserated with her as she voiced her displeasure at this latest intrusion. The overnight sedatives were obviously still being effective. One of the nurses thanked me for my help.

"The night nurse was right. You're like the guy in *The Notebook*."

I had no idea what she was talking about.

Around eleven am, the porter came to transport Joan to the colonoscopy department. I was along for the trip. Because of my calming influence, it was agreed that I'd be at Joan's side until the procedure commenced.

"Just a couple of minutes," we were told upon our arrival.

After being logged in, we waited outside the procedure room. About ninety minutes later, Joan was wheeled into room. As the nurse prepared Joan, I asked what had caused the delay.

"Lunch time?

"No, it's just always so busy in here. Compare it to a golf course. Sometimes your tee time gets delayed."

I congratulated myself for not replying with one of the many golf/colonoscopy jokes that flashed through my mind. I stayed with Joan until all the prep work was completed.

"Get yourself a coffee, we'll find you when we're done."

I was just finishing one of Second Cup's pricey coffees and a just as pricy muffin when the specialist's assistant came to me.

"All done."

She led me back to the procedure room where the specialist greeted me.

"We did a full scope and didn't find any problems. We'll do an endoscopy tomorrow morning. Perhaps we might find something then."

Back at the ER there were still no beds available yet in the hospital.

"That took a long time," said the charge nurse.

"Yes, there was a frost delay," I replied.

She'd have to be a golfer to get the joke.

The charge nurse explained to me that they were trying to get Joan into one of the wards. We had another visit from the young lady doctor. Her mentor had missed seeing Joan because she was downstairs. Hopefully, he'd see her later.

While Joan slept, I overheard the charge nurse at her station, phoning one of the wards.

"You've got to have a bed for this lady. Her husband is the guy from *The Notebook*."

She came back into the room.

"We'll probably be able to move Joan later this afternoon."

"Thanks," I said. "What's this, guy from *The Notebook* thing?"

"Have you read the book?"

"What book?"

"*The Notebook.*"

"Who's notebook?"

This was turning into an Abbott and Costello routine.

"It's a book, they made a movie from it. It's about a guy, his wife has dementia."

"Oh, no, I haven't."

That's as far as I wanted to go with this conversation.

Around 4:30, Joan was awake, a little bit drowsy. She wasn't in any way delusional. The charge nurse came into the room.

"We're moving you, Joan. You're going up to the fourth floor. Unit 401."

That was the same unit that Joan was in 2001. The porter steered the bed out into the passageway. I picked up Joan's stuff, including her lovely flowers, and off we went.

Room 418, I couldn't believe it. The same room. The same lovely view. This time the mountains were obscured by heavy precipitation. A mix of rain and snow.

"It's called sleet," I explained to the two young Filipina nurse's aides, sleet was a new word for them. The nurse entered. I introduced myself, mentioning that Joan was in the same room eight years ago.

"I was here then. Didn't you donate a piano?"

"It was an organ."

"Yes, that's right. What a small world we live in."

I spent the next three hours with Joanie in her new room. We watched the snow blowing and swirling against the big window. I was glad I'd picked the little daffodils. They wouldn't have survived the cold.

Joan was comfortable and there was no erratic behavior. The young doctor and her mentor visited. They confirmed that an endoscopy was scheduled for Joan on the following morning, which was Friday.

Around 8:30 pm, I checked with the nurse at her station.

"Has a sedative been prescribed for Joan?"

"Yes."

"Can I suggest that you give it to her now?"

I explained that I'd be leaving soon. My departure may create a situation where Joan would react badly and become unruly. Every patient on the unit would be disturbed.

"Good idea."

Sitting at Joan's bedside while the drug was administered intravenously, I watched Joan's eyes gradually closing. Within five minutes she was sleeping peacefully.

"That stuff's dynamite."

"It sure is," said the nurse.

I left a big note.

"Love you Joanie, see you at seven-thirty. Ronnie."

My van was covered in frozen snow. It took about fifteen minutes to clear the snow and ice and a few minutes more to warm the van. I arrived home after a thirty-minute, white-knuckle drive.

My Friday morning drive back to the hospital was a little easier. The roads were still icy but they'd been cleared of the heavy spring snow.

A smiling nurse was sitting with a wide awake Joan when I arrived a little after 7 am.

"Joan got your note."

Joan also got her expected kiss from me.

At mid-morning, the porter came to wheel Joan downstairs to the Endoscopy department.

"Back again?" said the receptionist.

"Yep, we're going to try the other end," I replied.

I'm sure they were used to that kind of humor. I'm just as sure that Joan didn't get the joke. There were no delays this time and I was only halfway through my coffee when the specialist waved me into the room.

"We've spotted what the problem is. Look at the screen."

He described to me the lesion that was visible on the screen. I'm not sure whether he said it was on the small intestine or the large one. I silently speculated that Joan's violent retching in the days prior to her visit to our doctor may have caused it.

"Joan, would you like some ice cream?" The nurse asked when we were back in the unit. Joan nodded. She was still groggy from the medication.

"We have to see if you can swallow."

Joan pretended to swallow.

"Close enough," said the nurse.

A little later, the young doctor entered with her mentor.

"There's nothing more we can do for Joan."

She was telling me that there was no way of treating Joan's problem at the hospital. Time would take care of it. However, someone needed to work on her communication skills. Her opening sentence sounded like Joan was at death's door.

"How do you feel about taking Joan home today?"

Joan's reaction made the decision really easy for me. She'd seen enough of this place.

"Come into the office."

It was just across the hall.

"We'll do the paperwork, write a prescription for Joan and give you some instructions."

Joan was dressed, sitting on the bed, and ready to roll when I stepped back into her room.

"Come on Joan, let's go home," I said

She gave me a big smile.

Late on Friday afternoon, we hugged after we stepped into our home. I took Joan into the bedroom.

"Let's have a nap, Joanie. I'll make us something to eat later."

I took off her topcoat and beloved blazer. Joan still had the intravenous shunt in her arm. I couldn't blame the nurses. Joan was going home and she'd put her coat on, end of story. I took Joan back to the hospital unit the next morning. We had the shunt removed. No remonstrations, no histrionics. Life's too short.

We got back to our routine pretty quickly. Joan recovered her strength and her appetite. My life was now centered on Joan's dementia and trying to keep her happy.

Chapter Fifty-eight

I did my best to keep our lovely house neat and tidy.
Joan wasn't much help in that endeavor. Her little corner
of the den needed daily attention. I supplied her with
some pens and a note pad to encourage her to write.
She'd tear out the pages, cut them into quarters, and
make smaller note pads, writing down the occasional
word that she copied from the TV screen. She discovered
that she could take the pens apart. Pretty soon, her tab-
letop was covered with various pen parts.

Facial tissues were another preoccupation. Joan
would pull each tissue out of the box, neatly fold it
twice, and place it on a pile on her table. I was told later
that this was commonplace with dementia sufferers.
She'd also wrap her earrings, jewelry, and rings in the
tissues. We lost a lovely pair of gold dollar earrings, an
heirloom from Joan's grandmother. I think they went out
with the used tissues. The loss solved a dilemma for me.
Which of Grandmother's many female descendants
would receive the precious earrings?

Even as Joan's condition worsened, I tried to
keep her neat and tidy. Each day, she wore one of her
favorite tops, navy pants, and comfortable shoes. Her
hair was always brushed and combed. A nice pair of gold
earrings usually complemented the brooch on her favorite navy blazer, the one with the silver buttons.

Through the years I'd seen too many dementia sufferers looking pathetic and unkempt. That wasn't going to happen to my Joanie. Eventually and inevitably, Joan either broke or lost most of her earrings.

"Don't worry Joanie, we'll go to Walmart and buy you another pair."

In the jewelry department, the clerk directed me to the ear rings display. I saw a card of about eight pairs of earrings. They were all similar to Joan's preferred style.

"How much are these?"

"$5.95."

That sounded very reasonable.

"I'll take this pair."

"It's $5.95 for the whole card, sir."

Back in the den, Joan had fun trying on the different pairs. It was the best six bucks I'd ever spent.

I gave Joan some privacy in the bathroom but not all of the time. Cleanliness came before dignity. One evening, Joan was alone in the bathroom. She seemed to be awfully quiet.

"Are you okay Joanie?"

When she didn't answer, I walked in. She was combing her hair. The problem was, instead using of a comb or brush, she was using my safety razor. My poor Joan. She looked so forlorn. It was lucky that I intervened when I did. She'd done some damage but it could have been much worse. I made light of the situation.

"No big deal Joanie. Let's go into the den. I'll clean this mess up."

What else could I have said? Joan wore a hat when we were outside the house until her hair grew back.

Life wasn't all gloom and doom. There was still a little joy, just not as much as there used to be. Joan and I were constantly together. Shopping, visiting friends, banking and medical appointments. We were inseparable, by necessity.

Our friends always enjoyed Joan's company. She was at her best with people. The various doctors we visited always had a place for Joan to sit in their examination rooms. Everyone was friendly, courteous and most of all, respectful.

Joan had cataract procedures on both of her eyes not long before her dementia surfaced. Her eyesight became excellent. Much later, we visited our optometrist for my routine check-up. I seated Joan below the eye chart screen. This would prevent her from saying the letters out loud as my eyes were tested, something she'd done on one of our previous visits. The doctor asked me to read one of the lines of letters. Joan beat me to it. She read all of the letters on each of the lines from top to bottom. The doctor cracked up. Joan was reading from the tiny monitor on his desk. It was more that twelve feet away from where she was sitting.

Chapter Fifty-nine

Visiting friends and family were always very welcome. I needed the support they brought with them. Joan would be negative before our guest's arrival.

"What do they want?"

Joan switched on the charm as soon as guests arrived. She usually put on a good show for everyone. Sometimes, she'd give me one of her looks.

"Don't these people have homes to go to?"

The short, usually unannounced, visits from our friends from Acadia Pool were always a lovely surprise. Joan enjoyed receiving the lovely Christmas cookies from Dara, the spicy Dutch cookies from Yoka, and the exotic dark chocolate from Donna. Yoka, a retired senior lifeguard, taught Joan to swim, so many years ago. Dara was a school teacher, our beloved aquazice instructor and a very caring friend. Donna, a widow, one of Joan's friends from the class, was special. She marched to the beat of her own drummer. That's why Joan loved her.

Visits from our friends from High River were always eagerly anticipated. Joan was herself and at ease whenever Ralph and Lucille came to see us. We'd been friends for so many years. Our friendship began when Lucille and I both became employed at the Cash and Carry in late 1973. We probably came together as a foursome at the company's Christmas party at the end of that year. The four of us grew closer as the years went by. Joan and Ralph used to help out at our Cash and Carry's semi-annual inventory counting events. Ralph criticizing Joan for her lack of counting skills. Joan always got right back at him.

"At least I know what I'm doing. You're just a plumber."

Actually, he was a pipe fitter. They teased and kibitzed each other on every possible occasion. It never ended, all through our long lasting friendship. Lucy Maude Montgomery would have called them kindred spirits. Lucille and I had the same kind of partnership although ours was more civilized. We had the same sense of humor and we'd often share private jokes. We speculated that the other office ladies probably thought we had something going on. We also had a strong working relationship with each other and with our boss, Bill Hall. We were a good management team.

On one occasion, after I became the store manager, I invited Lucille to accompany me to a trade show in Edmonton. We would be ordering seasonal goods for later shipment and it would be an overnight stay. I told her to bring Ralph and I'd be accompanied by Joan. We had separate rooms in one of Edmonton's best hotels. Lucille and I attended to business while Ralph and Joan got bored and toured the town. We met later for dinner. The next day, checking out of the hotel, the clerk put the amounts of the two rooms onto my bill. Back in Calgary, I attached the receipt to an expense request without indicating that it was for two rooms. I gave the request to one of my clerks for processing. We had lots of fun imagining the comments being made in the coffee room.

Lucille and Ralph changed residences a couple of times in Calgary. Eventually, after retiring from the work force, they settled into a beautiful single story residence in High River. Their new home was less than forty minutes south of our place so they still visited with us regularly. We drove to High River just as often.

Even as Joan's condition became more pronounced, Ralph continued his tormenting. She'd retaliate with all sorts of dire threats. Now, she gave him a sly wink as she ended each tirade. Ralph asked if could help her count her money.

"No way, I haven't got any," Joan replied.

The next minute she'd be flashing her stash at him, putting it back in her purse before he could grab it. Joan really had fun with Ralph. I was so happy to see my Joanie laughing. Our High River trips and our good friends' return visits were very welcome respites from our day-to-day struggles.

Chapter Sixty

Our extended family in Calgary were very supportive. These were nieces and nephews, all on my side of our family. None of Joan's siblings had followed her to Canada. They had no desire for a new lifestyle in the colonies.

Chris, my godchild, the youngest of the three Torley girls, and her husband Rob, were my designated go-to people. They lived just twenty minutes away. Anything I needed, they got. Anything I needed help with, they were always there for me.

I disseminated information to the family regarding Joan's health through Chris. She also passed on my wishes regarding the family's involvement in the lives of their Auntie Joan and Uncle Ronnie. Everyone was to enjoy their lives with their families. Uncle Ronnie would look after Joan, no problem. If and when, I'd need their help, I promised I'd ask. I wasn't asking them to 'butt out,' only to let me have some space to care for their Auntie Joanie.

Sylvia, now the matriarch of their family since the death of their dear mother and my sister Lil, was confined most of the time to a continuous care center on the far north part of Calgary. Her function was to organize any family help that I might ask for. We visited her occasionally, mostly to assure her that I was coping just fine. After having a successful career in senior's welfare, Sylvia's main concern was the wellbeing of her favorite seniors, Uncle Ronnie and Auntie Joan.

Marg, the middle sister and husband Paul, although continuously busy at their conference center, always found time to visit and admire Joan's garden.

"Anything you need, Uncle Ron? House cleaning? Washing?"

Frank and Pam, my deceased elder brother's son and his wife, were the closest, geographically speaking. They lived in the same part of town as Joan and I. We'd assisted them when they immigrated in 1976 when they were newlyweds. They now had a son, Frankie, and a daughter, Jennifer, plus two grandchildren. Frankie had two children. His son, Francis, was the fifth first-born of his family to carry his great, great, grandfather's name. Little Katie had Joan's mother's name. That made my Joanie really happy.

In 2013, Frank and Pam hosted a well-attended family celebration for my eightieth birthday in their lovely Deer Ridge home. I stored some wonderful pictures of the four generations of our family in my computer. I will always have the lovely memories of Joan enjoying the family that loved her so much. Frank and Pam would be my go-to people if a dire emergency ever demanded it.

My younger sister Sylvia lived in Parksville on Vancouver Island. She'd moved there from Calgary thirty years earlier. John and Lil sponsored her and her family's immigration in 1978.

Sylvia and I kept in touch by email and the occasional phone call. Her husband, Bill, was considerably older than Sylvia and in poor health. His disability meant that it was unlikely that they'd ever be visiting Calgary. Sylvia had four children from her first marriage which had ended in divorce. Her second husband died of a severe heart attack not long after their marriage. Her children all live in North Calgary.

I mentioned that none of Joan's family wished to live in Canada. Through the years, some of the family accepted invitations to visit Joan and me in Calgary. We were always so glad to see them. Their visits enabled Joan and me to share the many tourist attractions that abound in Southern Alberta. It was also wonderful for Joan to connect with her own immediate family.

In 1976, our first visitor was sixteen-year-old John. He was the fourth child of George and Kitty, who had seven children. John was a member of a youth boxing team from Merseyside. Competing against various teams of young men from Southern Alberta, the Liverpool boys had the experience of their young lives. John and one of his teammates stayed with us for the duration of their two-week tournament.

Bill and Maureen visited us in 1987. Their three-week stay was a lot of fun. We did the whole tourist thing, in Banff, Canmore, Heritage Park, and the Calgary Stampede Parade. Maureen loved the Stampede breakfasts. Bill also thought it was a splendid idea to have beer with his pancakes and breakfast sausages.

Our next visitors were George and Kitty. They split their 1988 holiday. The first half of the month-long vacation was spent in Winnipeg visiting their third child. George, an extremely intelligent young man, he had graduated with honors with a doctorate in medicine.

We had a wonderful fortnight together. The natural beauty of the Rockies enthralled Kitty. The Badlands that surround Drumheller in dinosaur country scared her. The stark landscape made her nervous. George, in typical

Liverpool style, took it all in without much comment. I knew that when he got back to his local pub in Liverpool he'd be extolling about all that was wondrous in Canada to anyone that would listen.

Driving three hundred miles to experience West Edmonton Mall, the largest shopping mall in Canada, was somewhat puzzling to George. I didn't see much sense in it either. The ladies loved it. Our three-hour journey, each way, gave us a lot of quality time together so that was a bonus.

Joan's younger brother Jim, his wife Elaine, and their youngest two children, Mathew and Amy, came to visit in 1995. Their eldest daughter Laura opted for a trip to Australia instead. Of course we had to go to the Tyrell Museum to see the dinosaurs. Amy, a quick witted, outgoing twelve-year-old, could name every one, plus a few fictional ones she invented as we toured the impressive displays.

"What was the shy one's name?"

"Doyouthinkhesaurus."

We had a wonderful day golfing in Canmore. Amy and her mom had the best fun racing the golf carts. It was a good thing that the course marshals were having a day off.

Maureen, now a widow, accompanied George and Kitty on their 1999 trip to Calgary. They'd be staying with their son, George and his family. George was now a professor and head of a cancer research department at the University of Calgary. He'd later become the Dean of Health Sciences at Purdue University in Indiana. Maureen would spend the two weeks with us.

After we picked them up at the airport, we had a lovely reunion party in the garden of George's beautiful rented home in Northwest Calgary.

On this holiday, we did less of the tourist attractions. Instead, we spent long days in our garden, mostly talking and laughing about the good old days of the past. It was as though we knew that this might be the last time we'd all be together as a family.

A couple of years later, 'Young' George mentioned to me that he'd noticed that his dad was showing signs of early onset dementia.

Chapter Sixty-one

Doctor Stinton insisted that we continue to see him at monthly intervals. He was keeping his eye on me as much as he was checking Joan's dementia. He had told me earlier that it would be my decision when we should seek the help of Alberta Health.

I was fully aware that taking care of Joan for all of those years was affecting my own health. As Joan's dementia worsened, when I was with Joan or we were with company, I was upbeat and cheerful. When I was alone I periodically found myself, miserable, and depressed.

I remembered that last scene in the movie *Iris*. I couldn't let that happen to Joan and I.

With a really heavy heart and after many sleepless nights pondering the probable outcome of my actions, I finally found the courage to ask Doctor Stinton to take that first step. My rationalization was that if I died or became sick looking after Joan, she wouldn't have me in her life. If Joan was in a care center, we'd still have each other.

"Well, how are the Freckletons today?" asked Dr. Stinton, when he walked into his little examination room with his customary greeting.

"It's time," was my simple reply.

He nodded. Through the years, we'd developed a sort of code that enabled us to talk about Joan's condition without her becoming agitated.

"You've done more than anyone could have expected," he continued. "I commend you for being able to make the decision now. I'd have advised you to do it earlier but it had to be your decision. You did an exemplary job, now it's time for you to take a break."

All this without mentioning Joan's name.

Doctor Stinton said he'd fill in the necessary paperwork. I could expect a call from a case worker within a couple of weeks. The caseworker would assess our needs and discuss the different scenarios that might evolve. He gave me the paperwork for some blood tests and chest X-rays.

"Alberta Health will need the results of these. Get them done as soon as you can."

I can't describe my feelings as I drove home. Joan was unusually quiet, perhaps she sensed what had just happened. I'd made the inevitable move. Now I had to live with myself. The doctors encouraging words about my fortitude offered little comfort. Would I ever forgive myself?

Chapter Sixty-two

I phoned Lucille and Ralph. I also emailed or phoned the different members of my family support group with the latest developments. I always tried to keep them informed. I felt that it was important for them to know that they were "in the loop." It was also important to me that I was maintaining contact with the people I loved. Their feedback was always so positive.

I took Joan to the medical labs for her blood tests and X-rays a couple of days later. There was no problem with the blood tests. Getting Joan's chest X-rayed was a challenge but we managed.

About ten days after our visit to Doctor Stinton, I received a phone call from a warm-voiced lady who introduced herself as Sandy. She was a case worker for Alberta Health Family Services. She asked if she could visit with us and review our situation. We agreed to meet at 2 pm on the following Monday. Sandy said that she'd arrange for a companion caregiver to sit in the den with Joan at the same time. We'd have the opportunity to have a candid conversation in another room without interruption.

About fifteen minutes after I'd introduced Joan to Jenny, a Filipina lady that would be Joan's companion for the duration of my meeting, Sandy arrived on my doorstep right on time. I estimated that she was in her late thirties. Weighed down by a large bulging brief case, Sandy greeted me with a warm smile and a firm handshake. It was easy to believe that she had a large case-load. She told me that she always carried all of her confidential documents with her. To lose them could result in a huge breach of confidentiality.

It was a miserable, icy cold day and Sandy was grateful for my offer of a cup of tea. After a brief chat with Joan and her new friend Jenny, Sandy and I retired to the living room.

Diving into her briefcase, Sandy pulled out a couple of folders and some blank forms. First came the questions. How long had I been coping? What kind of family support was I receiving? How was I managing? She proceeded to tell me about the home care system and what kind of help I could expect in the short term. Then she asked what did I need? I explained that dressing wasn't a problem and I could do that. I was keeping my promise to maintain Joan's dignity. I could continue with showering as well. Joan resisted me each time but we got it done. Health care workers weren't allowed to bathe any client that refused their help. Sandy asked if I needed housekeeping, but I said that I could do that too. If I scheduled a cleaner, I'd probably spend most of the day tidying the house before she came. Companion care was what I needed. Alberta Health would provide a companion for a couple of hours, two or three times each week. I'd be able to get out of the house and get a few things done without the worry of Joan and her unpredictable behavior.

Explaining to me that Joan would need to be assessed for suitability for admission to a care center, Sandy said that she'd call me in a couple of days. I'd only need to answer her questions with yes or no answers. I didn't need to worry about Joan listening.

"How do you feel about respite?" asked Sandy. "We can arrange for Joan to go into a local facility for a week or two. You'll be able to take a break. You can stay at home or go out of town, whatever you wish."

"Perhaps about ten days in early April?"

I thought I should take the opportunity offered. It was six months away.

"I'll start the ball rolling," Sandy replied. "Do you have any questions?"

"Yes, if Joan's assessment culminates in her suitability for being admitted into care, what would be the timeline?"

"You'll be asked to meet with a Transition Co-coordinator. She'll cover all the bases with regard to level of care, suitable locations, and costs. I don't know about the waiting time. I'm guessing about six months to a year."

I explained that I had an appointment with the Mitchell Eye Centre the following week. It was for a preliminary examination. I'd be undergoing cataract procedures on both eyes at a later date. I was informed by the scheduling clerk that the examining rooms were small. Joan would have to sit in the waiting room.

"No problem," said Sandy. "What date and time?"

"Next Tuesday at 8:30."

"A companion will be at your place at 8 am. She'll sit with Joan."

Sandy packed up her bulging briefcase and prepared to leave.

"Let me say goodbye to Joan and I'll be on my way. I'll call you soon, perhaps tomorrow."

Just before noon on the next day, Sandy called. She had just a few questions.

"Yes or no is good if Joan is sitting with you. We can start companion care. What days and times work?"

"Tuesdays and Thursdays from 2 to 4 pm would be good."

"Okay, we'll start the Thursday after your eye examination. Someone from WeCare will be calling you."

She asked a few more questions before reaching the final one.

"My last question. Do you think Joan needs to go into care?"

"Yes."

"You're doing the right thing. Based on my assessment of Joan's condition, your age, and the fact that you've taken care of Joan for so long, I'm recommending that we proceed with the next step. In the meantime, enjoy your life together as best you can."

She ended the call by telling me that she'd arranged respite for me. This was for ten days in April of the following year, 2014.

WeCare is one of the private companies contracted to Alberta Health Services. Its mandate is to supply home care professionals to clients in their homes.

I received a call on the day before my eye appointment. It was one of WeCare's managers. She explained how things worked, gave me a couple of contact phone numbers, and told me that a worker would be at our door tomorrow at 8 am. She mentioned that a companion caregiver would be sitting with Joan on the days and times programmed by Sandy, starting at 2 pm on Thursday, October 17.

The morning of my eye examination started on an edgy note. It was 8:15, the time I had booked the cab for, and the caregiver hadn't arrived. I'd been instructed to take a cab because I wouldn't be able to drive after the exam. They dilate the eyes as part of the procedures. The cab arrived and as I was convincing Joan that it was okay for her to sit next to the driver, the caregiver drove up. She explained that she'd made a couple of wrong turns and had trouble finding her way back on track.

"No problem, you can sit in the back with me."

I told the driver that we were going to the Mitchell Eye Centre. He knew where it was. I turned to the caregiver.

"My name is Ron; this is my wife Joan. Say hi, Joanie."

The caregiver, a shy, middle-aged First Nations lady, gave us both a very quiet 'Hi.' I explained that I needed her to sit with Joan while I had some tests. This was news to the caregiver, she'd been told that she was to be a home companion.

"Don't worry about it," I said. "We'll sort it out later."

I sat them both down in the crowded waiting area then reported to the receptionist. I quietly explained that my wife had dementia and that I'd brought someone to wait with her.

"Your wife can accompany you into each exam room. They're small rooms but we'll find an extra chair."

This was a nice surprise. It took almost two hours for Joan and I to visit all five of the rooms as the technician in each room performed a different set of tests. Everyone was equally friendly and respectful to Joan. The fifth room was actually the doctor's consulting room. Doctor Mitchell studied the results, examined my eyes and confirmed that I needed cataract procedures. We scheduled them for late March and early April. He said it would be okay for Joan to be present for the procedures.

It was a short, quiet ride back home. I was surprised and disappointed that the caregiver didn't engage Joan in any conversation. There was no interaction at all.

Sandy called later in the afternoon.

"Everything okay?"

I told her that everything went well but I hoped that she could arrange for a different caregiver on Thursday, stressing that it wasn't about ethnicity. Joan simply needed a more communicative, outgoing person.

"I understand," said Sandy.

Two days later, fifteen minutes before her scheduled 2 pm start time, our companion/caregiver arrived. A young Filipina, apologizing profusely for being early, introduced herself.

"Hi Jean, this is Joanie. I'm Ron."

"Hi Joanie, our names are nearly the same. You can call me Jeanie if you wish."

There was the communication that I was looking for, although there wasn't much interaction from Joan.

"Hi."

Joan was puzzled. I could almost read her thoughts as she wondered who this person was and why she was in our house? I didn't explain Jeanie's presence to Joan, explanations always brought more questions. I walked them back to the den, inviting Jean to sit in my chair next to Joan and perched on a stool facing both of them. Jean handed some introductory paperwork that WeCare needed me to have. It was formal information about the company and its services, plus their policies and expectations. I'd read them later.

There was no plan for me to leave our home during this first companion visit. I'd busy myself in another part of the house. I needed to know how Joan would behave when I wasn't by her side. I'd be available if necessary. After a few minutes of small talk, I left them watching the TV. After about ninety minutes, I returned to the den. There had been a little two-way conversation but nothing exciting. Joan was quietly fiddling with her treasures that were always on the table by her side.

I brought in some tea, cakes and cookies. Joan became a little more animated and seemed to be at ease. I encouraged Jean to tell us a little about herself. She had two jobs but no car. Her other job was as a caregiver in a care center. She was used to people like Joan.

Noticing that Jean didn't use the 'D' word, I thought this day's experience of a companion was positive. Next Tuesday I planned to leave Joan and Jean and venture out on my own for an hour or so.

Jean showed up on time on Tuesday.

"Hi, Joanie. How are you today?"

There was a small smile from Joan,

It was a lovely late autumn day. The sun had warmed up the sunroom. I guess that's why they call them sunrooms. I suggested to the ladies that it would be a nice place to spend the afternoon. After a few minutes, I explained to Joan that I had to go out for a few minutes. I had to see someone.

"I'll come with you."

"No, they've got a big dog. You don't like dogs. I won't be long."

I didn't want to sneak out. Who knows how Joan would have reacted?

The supermarket was crowded. I picked up the few things that we needed. Joining the checkout line-up, I quietly fumed about having to wait so long. In retrospect, my concern about being away from Joan was probably the reason for my anxiety. Returning home after less than an hour away, I was greeted by a stern-faced Joan.

"Where've you been?"

"I had to see one of the Old Timers. Picked up some groceries as well. I think we should have a cup of tea and some cake. I'll put the kettle on"

I took the loaded tray into the sunroom. Jean told me everything was good. Joan's face told a different story. We chatted for a while. I noticed Jean asked Joan questions that required 'thought out' answers. Perhaps Jean's experience with dementia sufferers was limited? 4 pm arrived and it was time for Jean to leave.

"Goodbye Joan, see you on Thursday."

"See you," said Joan, without enthusiasm.

The following Thursday, a car parked on the road fronting our home. A large black lady was rummaging in the trunk. I guessed that it was another caregiver so I went out to greet her.

"Mr. Freckleton? I'm Stella. Your regular caregiver isn't available."

"Hi Stella, please call me Ron. Before we go in the house, could I explain that Joan has dementia. She sometimes has the mind of a child. We're from England. When we were children, people had different attitudes and names for black people. Please forgive Joan if she says something inappropriate."

There was a huge smile from Stella.

"Don't concern yourself, Ron, I have lots of experience with dementia. Everything will be fine."

I loved this lady already. I took Stella into the house. Joan was sitting in her rocker in the den.

"Joanie, this is our new friend Stella"

"Hi Joan. May I call you Joanie?"

Stella really made our little den look even smaller. Joan's jaw dropped. Her mouth was open. Eyes wide, she didn't say anything.

Stella was from Ghana. She'd moved from California to Calgary just three years earlier. She hadn't lost her Ghanaian accent. She was big boned and tall with short curly hair and laughing eyes that matched her hearty laugh. She settled herself, at my invitation, into my easy chair close to Joan.

Pretty soon, we were all good friends. Stella made sure that Joan was part of the conversation. I explained to Stella that I had to go out.

"Me and Joanie will be fine, won't we, Joan?"

Joan wanted to come with me.

"I've got to go see the old guy with the big dog. You don't like dogs"

"I don't like dogs either," said Stella.

"Joan and I are staying here. We're going to watch a movie on TV."

Stella was in charge. That was fine with Joan. She had a new friend. I left the house feeling confident that my Joanie was in good hands. I was out for ninety minutes. The house was quiet when I let myself in. I could hear the soundtrack of an old movie. I put the kettle on and prepared our afternoon tea. Of course there was cake.

Entering the den, I found Joan and Stella exactly as I'd left them. Both were engrossed in the TV and the movie was just finishing. I hadn't seen Joan so interested in anything for quite a while.

While we enjoyed our cups of tea, Stella, at my prompting, told me about herself and her family. Coincidently, her married name was Harrison, the same name as my mam's parents. I didn't joke about us possibly being related. She had two children, both in their early teens. She was immensely proud of them and their academic achievements. Stella's husband, John, had been a qualified structural engineer in Ghana. In Calgary, he was a maintenance man in a local hotel.

Stella had credentials as a registered nurse and as a midwife in her home country and in California. She was waiting for them to be accepted in Alberta. She was only working part-time in her caregiving job. As she was leaving, I told her that we'd probably see her the following Tuesday.

Immediately after Stella left, I phoned Sandy, our case worker. I was prepared to leave a message but Sandy answered.

"We had a different caregiver today. She's the one I want to look after Joan."

Sandy was delighted when I described the afternoon's happenings.

"Sounds like you have a winner. I'll arrange everything with WeCare. Stella will take care of Joan"

Joan and I had our usual weekend. Nothing special. I had to clear snow off our driveway a couple of times as winter had decided to come early that year.

Stella's appearance at our door on Tuesday was an awesome sight. She was bundled up because of the cold, snowy weather. Her big quilted jacket made her physical dimensions even wider. She wore a bright multicolored West African-style knitted hat. It was pulled down to her eyes. Her big smile made her look like a genial giant and that's what she was. Taking off her outer clothing and her boots, Stella was wearing a very bright yellow top. She certainly was a very colorful lady. She told me how glad she was to be with us. She knew that I'd made it possible and thanked me profusely. I thanked her for what she did for Joan and we went into the den.

"Hi Joanie, my friend. How are you?"

Stella's greeting surprised Joan, who looked uncertainly at me.

"It's your new friend, Stella. Joanie, say hi."

"Hi Stella," said Joanie.

Joan's lack of short term memory meant that we were starting from scratch. It didn't take long though and Stella's laughter quickly put her at ease.

Knowing that Joan loved being photographed, I asked Stella's permission to take a picture or her with Joan in the front room. Joan posed, a big grin on her face, Stella, her perfect white teeth gleaming, holding onto her. It was a lovely picture but also the last one I'd take of Joan. What a treasure. What a memory for me to have, forever.

I had no reason to go out on that wintery day so I busied myself in the basement. Joan and Stella were content, watching another old movie on TV. Stella loved old movies and didn't receive that particular channel at her home. I went back into the den, shortly before Stella's quitting time.

"May I stay to see the end of the movie?" Stella asked.

November was a quiet, uneventful month. Stella was with her good friend Joan each Tuesday and Thursday afternoon. Joan's mood swings were becoming more frequent. Her angry moments soon passed. All that was needed was a big hug from me. She had no enthusiasm for anything, but wasn't morose, just disinterested. We had a couple of visits from Sandy, our case worker. They were just routine. She needed to know that we were doing okay.

The last Thursday of the month was our annual Old Time Salesmen's Christmas Luncheon. I was, and still am, the Secretary/Treasurer. I'd been railroaded into the position thirteen years earlier. None of the other old geezers would take the job, despite my pleading.

It was our group's 98th anniversary luncheon. It was the only time we got together each year. Since it was a gentlemen's luncheon, ladies weren't allowed.

For the previous four years, I'd taken Joan to the venue but we didn't stay for the luncheon. We'd held the event at the Elks Golf and Country Club in Northeast Calgary for a number of years. Prior to the luncheon, I'd help the directors to greet our members. There were usually about seventy attendees, although a decade earlier there had been more than one hundred. They say old soldiers never die yet our old time salesmen were popping off at an alarming rate.

A couple of the directors and I would register each arriving member and generally oversee the preparations for the luncheon. There were usually one or two little issues to sort out.

Joan was happy to sit and say hello to her many friends that she'd known for so many years. That year, she did a good job of faking it as she really didn't recognize anyone. Before the luncheon started, Joan and I left, as we'd done in the four previous years. We went home for our own lunch, returning as the meal was wrapping up. I'd pay the bill and we'd both greet the members. They were all Joan's best friends.

"Merry Christmas, see you next year."

In early December, with Stella looking after Joan, I had time to do a little Christmas shopping. Cookies and chocolates seemed to be the best bet. I could help Joanie eat those. I purchased a couple of nice tops, some briefs, and another nightgown. I bought her one every year. A lady can never have too many nightgowns.

Searching a number of stores for a suitable re-placement for Joan's beloved blazer with the silver buttons proved to be fruitless. In the past I'd purchased a number of cardigans. None had silver buttons so Joan rejected them all. As I write, I realize I should have sewn the silver buttons onto one of the new cardigans. Too late now.

I set up our little artificial tree on one of the coffee tables. The tree was about thirty inches tall with built-in lights. You plugged it in and you had instant Christmas. That year my limited gift wrapping skills showed no improvement. I rewrapped a number of Joan's gifts from the previous year to add to the growing pile, including a couple of pairs of slippers, still in their boxes. Joan had stopped wearing slippers and now wore low heeled, soft leather shoes around the house. I wrapped a beautiful scarf that Lucille had knitted. Joan had always loved lots of presents. I piled everything on the love seat next to the tree.

"All yours, Joanie."

December 15 was our 57th wedding anniversary. That year, we celebrated at Lucille and Ralph's home. Their home was beautifully decorated as it was every year. Lucille had some lovely seasonal placemats. Joan had crafted them many years ago and gifted them to Lucille. She wanted them back.

"They are mine"

"Okay Joanie, we'll take them home later."

We sat at the dining table for lunch. I signaled Lucille to hide the placemats and Joan forgot about them. Out of sight, out of mind.

Joan was more animated than she'd been for a couple of weeks. Ralph's teasing was responsible. We did a lot of reminiscing about past Christmases and there were lots of laughs. A lovely visit, over far too soon.

The following afternoon I received a call from Sandy.

"Will you give Cheryl of our Transition Services a call? You need to make an appointment," said Sandy, as she gave me the number. "She'll confirm my assessment and confer with you about next steps."

My good feelings after the lovely day in High River changed quickly into trepidation with the thought of taking another step closer towards Joan being moved into a care center. I tried to console myself. It wouldn't be happening soon. We'd probably have until the summer, but these thoughts didn't loosen the knots in my stomach.

I called Cheryl the following morning. We arranged to meet at 2:15 the following Thursday. I confirmed that I knew where her office was. It was less than a ten-minute drive from my home.

On time for my meeting with Cheryl, I sat in the large empty waiting area. She soon arrived, just a little late. She was a very friendly, obviously proficient, lady, slightly less than middle-aged and very professional. There was a minimum of small talk. First came the form filling, a necessary evil when government services are involved. Next, Cheryl told me that we'd have to visit our doctor. Joan had to be checked out, including blood tests since previous ones were outdated. The X-ray that had been done earlier was fine. Joan needed to be physically fit for acceptance into a care center.

Explaining the different levels of care available, Cheryl told me that Joan would be eligible for continuing care. Cheryl handed me a three-page list containing the names of all the care centers within a 50-kilometer radius of the city.

"You may choose any three centers on the list. Joan will be sent to the first available bed in any one of all of the centers listed. If it's not one of the three requested. Joan can be transferred when a bed becomes available. If you choose to refuse to accept the first available bed. Joan's name will automatically be returned to the bottom of the list."

I asked the inevitable question again.

"The wait time could be anything between four months and a year," said Cheryl. "You must be prepared to receive a phone call at any time."

The second sentence sounded ominous.

When I returned to our home, I called Doctor Stinton's office. Pearl, the office manager, answered, as always, cheerful and helpful.

" Yes Ron, I can squeeze you in tomorrow morning at 9.30."

"Merry Christmas."

I had a tin of shortbread cookies for Pearl and her assistant Debbie when Joan and I arrived on Friday morning. Pearl was Scottish and liked shortbread biscuits.

"Done your Christmas shopping yet, Joan?" Doctor Stinton asked.

Joan just laughed. He gave Joan a check-up, including her heart, blood pressure, and lungs and discovered no problems. Handing me the paperwork for blood tests, he told me that he'd be calling the mobile lab. They'd make a house call, probably in the New Year.

Chapter Sixty-three

Joan and I had a lovely Christmas. Stella was with us Christmas Eve. The three of us enjoyed an old Christmas movie on TV. We had two kinds of cake with our afternoon tea.

About a year earlier, I'd decided that I'd try my hand at baking cakes. Joan's expeditions to the Dollar Store had left us with a shelf full of all kinds of cake mixes. I thought I should do something to diminish them. Once again I'd discovered a hidden talent. I could bake cakes. Actually, all I did was follow the printed instructions, but that's an achievement for a guy.

I enjoyed listening to Joan as she sat at the kitchen table watching me doing all the prep work with the cake mix and the other ingredients.

"Where did you learn to cook? Aren't you clever? Did you used to be a chef?"

In the old days Joan wouldn't have let me anywhere near her blender.

As Stella left on Christmas Eve, I handed her some chocolates and a Christmas card.

"Don't open the envelope until tomorrow," I said.

I'd enclosed a $20 bill with the card. This was strictly verboten according to her employers but I wouldn't be telling them. Really, I mean really big hugs for both of us from Stella. I told her that she didn't have to work on Boxing Day but she insisted. She needed the hours and there was probably a good movie on our TV.

I tried to make our Christmas Day the same as all of the other Christmases that Joan and I had spent together. I stuck with the same routine. I was up early and got Joan into the bathroom. Everything went smoothly. Joan was happy. It was Christmas.

"What would you like to wear?"

Joan picked one of the three tops I'd chosen. Of course she had to wear her favorite blazer.

"Let's have breakfast, then we'll see what Father Christmas has left for us."

Yes, it was still Father Christmas. After more than forty years in Canada, we hadn't converted him into Santa Claus. I made a traditional 'Sunday' breakfast. We had scrambled eggs and a little piece of ham with our toast, our cereal, and the mandatary shared banana.

After breakfast we into the living room. The fire was lit and it took just a flip of the switch to transform the room. The lights were twinkling on our little tree and the love seat was piled high with wrapped Christmas parcels. Joan wasn't as excited as she'd been in previous years but she was happy. That made me feel so good.

I thought of the previous thirty-four years that we'd performed the same ritual in this house, the same love seat, the same everything. In the late 80s and early 90s I'd have the latest James Mitchener epic amongst my stocking stuffers. Joan had always insisted that we had at least six stocking stuffers and a major gift each. This year we had no discussion, no excited anticipation, no mock complaints.

"Where's my major?"

Joan made short work of her gift opening. The biggest boxes were dealt with first. Cookies and chocolates, lovely. Slippers were moved to one side with no comment, the same as the previous year. Joan loved the two six packs of underpants.

"Different colors, just what I need."

She couldn't have been more enthusiastic if they'd been diamond rings. There was no searching for a 'major.' Joan was content. After an hour or so, we moved into the den. Joan took her new panties with her. It was time to call Maureen and her family in St. Helens. They'd just about be finished their Christmas dinner. I put the phone on speaker. There were lots of Merry Christmases from everyone.

"What time is it there?" was always Maureen's opening question. There lots of chatter and laughter from both sides of the Atlantic.

"What did you get from Father Christmas?"

"New knickers," said Joan.

The prolonged goodbyes seemed longer than other years. Joan seemed pensive after I hung up the phone.

"I wonder how my Mam and Dad are."

I had to turn away as I answered.

"They're just fine, I'm sure."

Joan's Mam and Dad had both passed away more than thirty-five years earlier.

"I'll make a cup of tea and a sandwich."

I moved into the kitchen. I didn't want Joan to see my tears.

In the afternoon, I called my sister, Sylvia.

"Merry Christmas, our Ronnie. Give Joan a big hug from us."

We received a call from Lucille and Ralph. Of course Joan had to tell Ralph that she'd got new knickers for Christmas.

It was an early Christmas dinner that year. Turkey of course, in the living room. Christmas day was the only day of the year that we ate in there, we converted the desk into a dining table. For the first time ever, I hadn't roasted a turkey. It made more sense to buy a pre-cooked breast from the Co-op's Deli. That year there was no aroma wafting from the oven but Joan didn't notice. There was a special treat for dessert, English trifle, which I made myself, although with no custard. I didn't have the expertise to make custard. Ice cream was an acceptable substitute. We finished off the meal with crackers, cheese, and a glass of red wine. Life was good.

We sat quietly on the love seat listening to an old audio tape of the opening theme of the movie *Out of Africa*. It was lovely peaceful music. I imagined Joan and me sitting in tandem in that little biplane soaring over the Serengeti. Every year, the same music. Every year, the same dream.

A lovely Christmas. A lovely memory.

Boxing Day was nice too. We pottered around the house in the morning. I called my sister Elsie back in Liverpool.

"Merry Christmas."

I had to wish her Happy Birthday too. Her 92nd birthday was coming up on January 2, one day before my 82nd. We received and initiated phone calls from and to our Calgary families. Everyone had a nice Christmas.

I noticed Joan hiding her new panties behind her side table in the den. Nobody was going to steal them.

Stella showed up at 2 pm. There was another big hug and a big thank you for the gift.

"Yes, I know it isn't allowed. I won't tell anyone if you don't."

At 7:30 on the morning after Boxing Day I received a surprise phone call. It was the nurse from the mobile lab.

"I'm setting up my day's schedule. What time would be convenient?"

"Today?"

I really was surprised. I didn't expect things to be happening so fast.

"Anytime is good for us."

"See you between 9 and 10. Please have Joan's Alberta Health card ready."

A very proficient young lady arrived in a small car. She was ready to tend to Joan right in the hall.

"No, let's go into the living room, we'll be more comfortable there."

She politely declined my offer of coffee or tea.

"Heavy schedule today, Lots to do."

She took Joan's samples with no resistance then she was off to the next call within minutes of arriving.

Joan and I spent New Year's Eve in the den. It was another nice quiet evening. We had our shower battle the night before, so tonight would be peaceful. There was nothing much on TV, just the old recycled stuff. It seemed to be the same as the year before.

Joan was wearing her new nightie. We talked about past New Year's Eves. At least I talked, Joan sat quietly. I think she was happy listening to my voice. I never asked her to confirm my spoken memories. Why shatter the tranquility?

A little later, around 8 o'clock, I prepared our ritualistic New Year snack. Cheese and crackers with a glass of Merlot for Joan, a Rusty Nail for me. A Rusty Nail is a cocktail, one-part Scotch, one part Drambuie, with lots of ice.

We were in bed by nine. The boisterous days of bringing in the New Year at midnight were long gone.

"Happy New Year."

Friday January 3 was a big day. It was my 81st birthday and Lucille and Ralph came to help us celebrate. I bought a fruit and cheese platter plus a $10 birthday cake from the Co-op. Lucille and Ralph brought a large gift bag full of trinkets for Joan. She was delighted. I pretended to sulk.

"Hey. It's my birthday."

We had a really great party. Lucille and Ralph made sure of that. They knew, as I did, this was probably our last celebration as a group of four.

My birthday signaled that it was time to get started on my basement gardening activities. I pretended that this year would be no different.

We had a couple of easy chairs and a large TV in the basement living room. I usually parked Joan there while I did my horticultural thing. She had the option of watching me work or watching TV. When she got bored with one, she would watch the other. When she got bored with both, I'd quit my gardening and we'd go back up the stairs.

"Keep Joan happy," as Doctor Stinton said.

The next couple of days passed slowly. We enjoyed watching the snow fall in the back yard. Everything looking so sparkling white and pristine. I didn't enjoy having to shovel the same white stuff off the front driveway.

The snow stopped and we had two or three days of mild Chinook conditions. Weather and wind anomalies over the Rockies sometimes produced unusually balmy weather in and around Calgary. *Chinook* is a First Nations word for Snow Eater. Some of the snow disappeared but the cold temperatures returned us to winter far too quickly.

Monday, January 13 is a date imprinted in my memory. I hated the number 13. I'd just finished a stint of seed planting in the basement. Joan and I were partaking in a restful afternoon in our cozy little den. The phone's ringing jarred me from the drowsy state I was enjoying.

"Mr. Freckleton?"

Why did my pulse quicken?

"My name is Annabelle. I'm calling from Chinook Park Care Centre."

Now my stomach was knotted.

"We have a bed for Joan."

With Joan close at hand, I had to try to sound normal. Joan knew when I was upset. I didn't want her upset too. I may have said okay or fine, I don't remember. I certainly didn't say that it was good.

"Would you bring Joan tomorrow?"

"We'll come on Wednesday," I replied.

"No, it has to be tomorrow."

"Okay, we'll be there at 2 o'clock."

'No, please come at 9 am."

Obviously she was familiar with procrastinators.

I told Annabelle that we'd be there. The one positive note was that I had no time at all to dwell on the future.

Chapter Sixty-four

On Tuesday, January 14 we left our house at exactly
8:45 am. As I locked the door, I thought that this might
be the last time that Joan would see our home. The home
she loved, the home we'd lived in for thirty-five years. A
thin coating of fresh snow covered the driveway. I
stopped the car halfway down.

"Doesn't the border look pretty in the snow?"

I was giving Joan one last look.

On our drive to the care center, I tried to chat
with Joan. I knew that if I stayed silent she'd know
something wasn't right. She showed no interest in where
we were going but I wasn't alarmed. Lately, Joan didn't
seem to have much curiosity about anything.

"We're going to the doctors, Joanie, It's not far."

I was trying to sound upbeat but inside, I was in
turmoil. My stomach was in knots. What was I doing to
my dear Joan?

Luckily, the traffic was light. We arrived right on
time at a tidy three-story brick building with lots of windows. I was able to park outside the main entrance. Joan
was reluctant to get out of the car. Had she read my body
language? She always could. Had she seen the signage
for *Chinook Park Care Centre* as the car turned into the
driveway? I took her walker out of the rear of the van.

"Come on, Joanie. Let's see what's happening."

Chapter Sixty-five

The warm foyer led to a large, wide hallway. The reception desk was a few yards inside. A young Asian lady behind the desk was bright and cheery. I introduced myself and Joan. I doubt that I sounded bright and cheery, but I tried. Joan had become unusually quiet. My stomach knotted even tighter.

Annabelle, the facility manager, came out of her office. I'd spoken to her when she phoned the day before. She must have recognized my voice. Her office was alongside the reception desk. I correctly guessed from her accent that she was from the Philippines.

"Good morning, lovely to see you, Joan," she introduced herself.

Joan seemed to brighten up.

"Hi."

I knew my Joan, she was suspicious.

"You're walking."

Annabelle was surprised. I was surprised that she was surprised. "Let's go up to Park Place, I'll show you around"

The care center had three floors. The ground floor was inhabited by Assisted Living residents. Park Place on the second floor was the domain of those in need of Continuing Care. The third floor was the Hospice. We took the elevator. A couple of smiling young ladies, Christine the nurse and Emma the nurse's aide, both Filipina, were waiting to greet us. We trooped into a nearby room just a few steps from the elevator. Joan was to share this room with one other resident until a private room became available.

"It's not much of a waiting list."

"This is your bed, Joan, right by the window."

"Like hell it is!" said Joan.

We continued the tour. In the dining room we drew curious stares from some of the residents, who were just finishing their breakfasts. Situated almost opposite Joan's room, the dining room was big and bright. Large windows, the length of the outside wall, were the source of the brightness in the room. Six vinyl-topped tables, each able to accommodate four diners, were spaced more or less evenly on an uncarpeted floor. A very large, wall-mounted TV took up most of one of the other walls. The fourth wall was fronted by the serving counter.

Further along the hallway, past a number of resident's rooms, was the nurse's station, which always fully staffed. Opposite was another dining room, a little bigger than the first one. There were more stares from a couple of stragglers finishing breakfast.

"Good Morning."

The unit housed about forty residents.

Around the corner was the doctor's office.

"Doctor Olibanji is here all day, every Wednesday."

The unit manager's office was next on the tour. Eileen introduced herself and joined our group.

Joan has become more relaxed and animated. I think she was putting on a show. We walked into a large multi-purpose room. Although it was called the Activities Room, there wasn't activity, in fact the room was empty. There were three or four easy chairs and side tables. Half-a-dozen straight-backed chairs were around a bigger table, others against the walls and there was another big TV on the wall. Opposite, a large window faced the busy world below. In one corner of the room stood a large bookcase, well stocked with books of all shapes and sizes. Joan loves books. Did I think she'll read any of them? No, I didn't. Our tour finished at the polished steel door of the second of the building's two elevators, situated in an alcove at the end of the hallway.

As we retraced our steps, Joan spotted an old piano parked by the unit manager's office.

"Let's sit down and play the piano," I suggested.

Joan didn't need coaxing. She sat on the stool, ran her fingers up and down the yellowed ivory keys then started to play. The music wasn't in the lovely fashion that she used to play, or that I was used to listening to, but the tunes were recognizable and still melodic. There was only a little bit of showing off. The staff were delighted. One of the group even joined Joan on the long piano stool.

While Joan was distracted. I whispered to the unit manager that I was leaving. I'd leave Joan's bag at reception. I promised that I'd be back at 1 pm.

In my sleeplessness the night before, I'd tried to envisage a scenario where I'd be able to leave without histrionics. The script couldn't have been written better.

Walking back to the elevator, I was able to observe some of the residents. Two or three were ambulatory, pushing their walkers, others were in wheelchairs, each parked beside the door to their room. All suffering the various stages of dementia.

"Good morning," I said.

Some responded, some didn't. A bleak future for my Joanie.

"Joan's safe now. Everything will be okay," I told myself as I was driving home.

"Like hell it will!" I answered myself in Joan's words.

I packed some more items Joan might need into a small bag. I included a digital picture frame with a USB memory stick containing pictures of the beautiful flowers in our garden, plus a few pictures of Joan enjoying the flowers. I wondered if she'd appreciate them.

Having no reason to hang about the house until 1 pm, I was back at the care center at 12:30. I parked in the same spot. Joan was sitting alone in the otherwise empty dining room. Lunch had been served and I guessed that the other residents were back in their rooms. I didn't know if Joan had eaten. I didn't ask.

"Hi, Joanie."

"Hi."

She was pleased to see me but not overjoyed.

"Come on, we'll go to your room."

Joan didn't budge. I tried helping her out of the chair. She was doing the dead weight thing. The chair moved but Joan didn't. I took one arm and tried again.

"Don't do that," a stern-voiced aide said. "Are you her husband?" She put her arm around Joan's arm-pit and directed me to do the same on the other side. Together, we were able to get Joan upright.

"Here, what's her name?"

"Joan."

"Here, Joan, take hold of your walker."

That was Laine. We'd gotten off on the wrong foot. Within a couple of days, we'd be friends. She was another Filipina and a really caring caregiver.

Joan and I walked to her room and sat on the bed together. I took her hand.

"Everything will be alright, Joanie."

Joan remained silent. A short time later Christine entered the room. We needed to complete the necessary paper work associated with Joan's admittance to the care center. Joan sat quietly on the bed. I wondered what she was thinking. Perhaps it was better that I didn't know.

Joan's half of the room was reasonably spacious. Her hospital-style bed paralleled the large window look-ing directly down to the main entrance. A light wood bedside table, a matching chest of draws and a wardrobe comprised all of the furniture. There was more storage space than Joan would need. There was also a sturdy chair.

The room's other occupant was a quiet elderly lady. She didn't communicate much. I learned later that during the day she was usually out of the room and when she was in the room, she spent the time sleeping. Her side of the room was a mirror image of Joan's side, ex-cept that she had a wall instead of a window. A heavy curtain separated the spaces when privacy was required. The large bathroom close to the door completed the amenities of the room.

We sat awhile, my arm around Joan's shoulders. I held her hand. I kissed her cheek and she pulled away just a little. I suggested that we take a walk. I had to help her stand. We walked in the same direction as our morning tour. There were lots of smiles from staff members, a couple of residents gave us curious looks. For once, dementia was on my side. Joan seemed to accept that where we were, was okay. Perhaps soon, she wouldn't remember our home. Those thoughts did nothing to alleviate the huge burden of guilt that I carried.

When the afternoon shift started, Joan's new caregivers introduced themselves with big smiles. Connie and Marcela were both born in Manila.

"Where would I be without 'Me Amiga's' from the Philippines?" I thought, convinced that Joan was in good hands.

A large percentage of the care center's staff were from the Philippines. I quickly learned the key phrases connected with greetings in their language of Tagalog. I also memorized most of their names. It didn't take long to make friends with all of them.

Just before supper, I asked Connie to distract Joan while I left. I tried to use that method of leaving on every occasion. Saying goodbye may have caused Joan distress, however short-lived. Why risk it? I'd given her a kiss. She just didn't know that it was her goodnight kiss.

I discovered a ticket on my windshield when I reached my car. Who knew it was a park-and-pay zone?

Home alone for the first time since Joan was hospitalized two years earlier, I felt empty. It had nothing to do with not eating. I roamed around the house for a while, not quite sure of what I should be doing. Eventually, I made myself some scrambled eggs and a couple of pieces of toast. I told myself that I'd feel better tomorrow. Could I feel worse? It was a very long night. I got as much sleep as I'd had the night before and was out of bed before 5 am. I didn't feel better.

Arriving at the care center just before 9 am, filled with trepidation, I wondered what would be waiting for me. Joan was having breakfast in the crowded dining room. She saw me and a big smile broke out. I gave her a big kiss. She insisted on another one. Where had I been?

"I just had to slip out for something."

Joan was good with that.

After breakfast, we walked the whole length of the unit, Joan using her walker. It was good exercise for both of us. At the far end of the unit, we rediscovered the piano. Joan sat on the stool and I sat beside her. She played a little. She tried to pick off the sticker that someone had glued onto the Middle C. We talked a little. A little kiss, another little kiss. She played some more.

After an hour or so it was time for another walk. This time back to our room, with more smiles from the staff.

"We heard you playing the piano, Joan. You play well."

There was a little smile from Joan, a big grin from me.

We held hands as we sat on Joan's bed until it was time for lunch. Looking at the pictures of the flowers, Joan pretended to be interested. I felt that I'd regained her trust. I hoped I had.

A little later, after lunch, while Joan slept, I had a scheduled, in-depth meeting with her new doctor. I answered Doctor Olibanji's questions referencing Joan's medical history. As I talked, she was assessing my well-being, making sure that my expectations weren't overly optimistic.

"Joan will not get better. Dementia never improves. Enjoy what you both have for as long as you are able to."

That was the message, delivered in perfect English with just a hint of Nigeria.

Joan was awake when I returned. My hugs and kisses were a little more meaningful. I stayed with her until just before suppertime.

When I visited on our third morning at Park Place, Joan was awake and still in bed. She was pleased to see me, with just a little disapproval in her greeting.

"Where have you been?"

A different nurse's aide had followed me into the room. Apologizing for being late, she explained that Joan had refused to cooperate earlier, so she'd attended to the other resident's needs.

Each nurse's aide had charge of six to eight residents. They all had to be in the dining room before 9 am. It was a really demanding schedule and the staffing levels were only just within the mandated guidelines.

Juliette, Joan's aide for today, managed to clean, body wash, and dress her. This was with my assistance, and not without some choice language and a lot of resistance from Joan. After a struggle to get Joan upright and a brief combing of her hair, we were ready for the dining room.

Breakfast usually consisted of juice and coffee, porridge or cereal, a boiled egg and toast, plus jam was available. Sometimes bacon or sausages were an added treat. It was good wholesome food, just not served in *Breakfast at Tiffany's* style. On that day, Joan chose just juice, an egg, and a piece of toast. She didn't eat all of it.

We took our long walk to the piano. It was good to see that Joan still enjoyed playing. I found solace in knowing that there was still a little joy in her life.

I stayed with Joan until after lunch, intending to return after a couple of hours.

I was eating my own late lunch at home when the doorbell rang. It was Stella. 2 pm was her scheduled start time to care for Joan. I'd called WeCare on Monday to cancel Joan's home care program. They misunderstood, thinking I was only cancelling for the next day. Poor Stella. I told her that Joan was in the care center and would be staying there. Stella stayed with me while I finished my lunch. I told her of the events that led up Joan's admittance to the care center.

This loving woman that Joan and I had met less than three months earlier was having difficulty holding back her tears. I assured her that everything would be okay. We hugged and I told her that I'd stay in touch with her. If she needed a reference, just call. We said our goodbyes again. As I drove back to the care center, I wished that I could tell Joan about Stella's last visit.

I stayed with Joan until after supper. She was sleeping peacefully when I left. On my way home at the end of that third day, I bought a small TV for Joan and installed it the next morning.

Planning a visiting schedule became important since I needed a daily routine. I intended to be with Joan for most of her meals. I'd be at her bedside each morning to assist in getting her ready for her day. Usually when I arrived between 7:30 and 8, Joan was awake. She was always glad to see me. I never forgot to give her the kiss that was expected. We'd spend the afternoons together and I'd leave for home after supper.

Joan had no interest in the TV that I'd installed or its programing. Not even Sesame Street, her favorite viewing just a few short weeks earlier. I inserted a memory stick containing the garden pictures that I'd used for viewing on the smaller digital picture frame into the TV. Now a continuous slide show filled the screen and enabled our lovely dahlias to be shared with Joan's caregivers.

Each day we did our daily walk to the piano, always encouraged by the staff.

"You're going to play the piano, Joan?"

Throughout the following weeks, Joan's piano expertise and her enthusiasm for playing diminished. On a couple of occasions, we joined a group in the activities room for gentle exercises with a very large inflated ball. Joan was a little too aggressive bouncing the ball. She also widened the group's vocabulary with her vocalization when the ball hit her. Once we joined a group of residents singing well known old songs. Large print song sheets were distributed. A recording machine produced the sound of a piano accompanied by a monosyllabic male voice. He was singing the songs in the same order as the song sheet list. Joan wasn't enthralled. The loudest and most enthusiastic singers were the recreational therapist conducting the singing and myself. I couldn't get *'She wore a tulip, a big yellow tulip'* out of my mind for weeks.

I memorized most of the caregivers' names. Why wouldn't I? These were the people taking good care of my Joanie. Always respectful and friendly, they allowed her as much dignity as their job permitted. My assistance with washing, dressing, and toilet needs was always appreciated.

"Why isn't my husband like you?"

I also enjoyed calling the other residents by name. Their returning smiles were always rewarding.

Joan's shower schedule was two showers each week, after supper on Wednesdays and Saturdays. I wasn't there for the first few attempts. Joan's vehement protests and physical resistance made it almost impossible for the caregivers to restrain her in the restricted area of the shower. Connie's face was a picture of happiness when I told her that I'd be in attendance for Joan's future showers.

I was told that it was an expression of the trust that Joan placed in me. My physical presence and familiar soothing voice were enough to quieten her, or at least lessen her aggressive behavior. I still had to hold her hands while Connie or one of her workmates worked their magic.

The same trust was displayed at meal times. Joan never wanted to eat. If I wasn't present, nothing would be eaten. Coaxing didn't work. If I was by her side, she'd eat a little but Joan had no interest in food. Because of her refusal to chew or swallow, perhaps she'd forgotten how, pureed foods became the norm. We tried the nutrition drinks without much success. Naturally, Joan's energy level was diminishing as her dementia worsened.

Sitting with Joan during mealtimes gave me an insight into the lives of the other residents. I could quietly observe them while I spoon-fed Joan. The less infirm, able to dress with the minimum of assistance, were always seated early. They each wore an identical bib and patiently waited for their meal to be served. Everyone had their designated place. Most were using wheelchairs or walkers. If a new caregiver wheeled in a resident and placed them in the wrong seat, a minor excitement would breakout as other residents found themselves in the wrong seat. I likened it to chaotic musical chairs without the music.

"What's for dessert?" George, a pleasant, quiet, elderly gentleman never failed to ask. It didn't matter if it was breakfast, lunch, or dinner.

A very needy lady sat at Joan's table, always complaining about the pain she was in. Her chair was uncomfortable; could she sit on the seat of her walker?

"Another coffee please, black." An often repeated request.

"She's a lucky lady," she said, noting the attention that I was giving Joan.

"Joan's my wife. I love her," I replied.

"Do you have a brother?" she asked, causing me to laugh out loud.

After lunch it became a routine for Joan to lie on her bed, whether she'd eaten or not. Soon she'd be sleeping and I'd take the opportunity to go home for lunch, catch up on stuff that needed to be done, or I'd just take a nap myself. I was always back with Joan well before suppertime.

Although I knew that our future wouldn't be getting better, I made plans to make our life as good as it could be. As soon as a private room became available, I'd install a big TV, Joan's keyboard, my recliner chair, and Joan's favorite rocking chair. I'd make Joan's room into our home. Of course I'd bring Joan's beloved collection of Catherine Cookson's hardcovers. I'd read to her for as long as she wanted me to. After four weeks, we hadn't made much progress up the waiting list for the much coveted private room.

Chapter Sixty-six

In late February, I thought about the viability of moving into a retirement residence on the same block as Chinook Park called the Trinity Lodge Retirement Community. I drove by the sign and the building every time I visited my Joanie. If things worked out, I'd be able to stay with Joan all day, every day, except for my meals and sleeping. I made the decision and arranged an appointment to tour the facility on a Sunday afternoon during Joan's nap time.

Always a planner, some would call me a dreamer, if I liked what I saw, I'd sell the house and move into Trinity Lodge on the first day of September. The plan was that I'd make that year's flower garden the best ever. In late August we'd have a garden party. All of our friends and family would be invited. Of course Joan would be there. She could oversee things from her favorite chair in the sunroom. I always shared my dreams with Lucille. She demanded that she help organize the garden party.

My nieces and nephews were all very supportive of me making a move towards a retirement residency. Chris and Rob told me how happy they were that I'd come up with the idea myself. They wouldn't have interfered with my choice of lifestyle but, being realists, they knew that sooner or later I'd be unable to cope with the twin difficulties of living alone and travelling to visit Joan two or three times each day.

"Better to jump than be pushed," Rob put it, as pragmatic as ever.

Trinity Lodge, originally built and run for the Baptist Church in 1975, was by that time a well-established, private property. It was one of a group of similar facilities, well managed by professionals and owned by a corporation. It was a really high quality, fully occupied, high-end retirement residence.

Recently modernized and extended, it was architecturally well planned. Part two-story, part four-story. It wasn't the austere, rectangular building normally associated with senior's accommodations.

The gabled main entrance was set back from a circular driveway, which was centered by a large floral island. Mature trees and bushes surrounded the building, as did a well-used pathway.

I was a couple of minutes early for my 1:30 appointment with Valerie, the Marketing Manager at Trinity. Seniors are always early for everything. I walked through the warm spacious vestibule leading to the entrance. A couple of residents relaxing on the benches after lunch greeted me with welcoming smiles.

The spacious and well-lit foyer reminded me of a high class residential hotel. Easy chairs and side tables lined the walls. A large, well-appointed dining room was visible through glass-paned, double doors. Richly colored carpeting added to the pleasant ambiance.

"Hi, Ron," a voice called, as I waited at the reception desk.

It was Emma, one of Joan's favorite caregivers.

"Hi, Ron," Debbie added.

"Hi, Ron," said yet another voice.

This time it was Mila. It seemed that all of Joan's caregivers from Park Place were working part of their day at Trinity Lodge. I think I was sold before I'd even met with Val.

Val arrived at the desk on time. A very smartly-dressed, slim, confident, and vivacious lady with lots of bling. She greeted me warmly with a big smile. I had a feeling that I knew her from a previous life.

We sat briefly at a polished table in a small conference room adjacent to the reception desk, a large window facing out onto a lovely courtyard. A digital picture frame on a side table flashed pictures of obviously happy residents. Testimonials and award certificates lined three walls. The door had glass panes that matched the dining room doors. The corporate mission statement centered the display, proclaiming that the residents were the number one priority.

After a quick discussion on my circumstances, needs, and aspirations, we were off on the grand tour. It disappointed me that Val never said that I looked too young to qualify for residency. As we walked through the spacious foyer, a gentleman was playing a grand piano. Residents were sitting around the large, well-furnished area, quietly appreciating the music.

"That's Doctor Hunter, his mother's a resident. He volunteers to play every Sunday."

"Here's the Bistro."

The large room looked like a very posh Starbucks without the self-important baristas. No laptop or smartphone addicts either.

"Residents and their friends can come in here anytime for a quiet coffee and a muffin. Anything they wish. Cookies, fresh juice, fresh fruit, different kinds of tea. They just help themselves."

I noticed there were no cash registers. That was a big plus.

We were still in the foyer where I noticed the mailboxes, with large pictures of newly-arrived residents above them. A notice board detailing all of the events scheduled for the month was displayed on the wall close to the elevator. There were also sign-up sheets for the various activities. There was lots of stuff going on. One of this week's outings was to Drumheller in dinosaur country.

"That's cute," I thought. "Taking the residents to see something that's older than they are."

Next came the recreation area. There was an extra-large TV in front of an orderly row of easy chairs. It was a small theatre. You could probably take a nap and nobody would notice. A pool table and a shuffle board bordered the space. Again, there were lots of easy chairs. It appeared that socializing was the number one activity and there was nothing wrong with that.

"Here's the gym. We have fitness classes or you can work to your own schedule."

It was another big room. A mirror along the length of one wall made the room look even bigger. The carpeted floor was covered by a variety of fitness equipment. Instructions on the proper use of each piece of apparatus were displayed on the walls.

"We have a tuck shop that seems to sell everything you'll need. You can reward yourself with a candy bar for all of your hard work in the gym."

Next to the tuck shop was the Chinook Room, another large well-furnished space. It was one of a number of venues available for special events. It was also the Chapel, a multi-denominational place of daily worship. The nurse's office completed this lobby portion of the tour.

"Lots of amenities," said Val.

I was impressed that such a large proportion of the space in the facility was allocated to the resident's social needs. This was not an old people's warehouse. Opposite the nurse's office, automatic sliding glass doors lead out to one of the courtyards.

"Let's walk through here. Isn't it lovely?"

The interior of the building was dissected by three distinctly different courtyards, each canopied by trees of all sizes. Bushes and plants bordered the meandering pathways. Ornamental artifacts added a touch of elegance. Of course, there were ample benches for those that wished to sit and absorb the serenity of it all. I pictured myself, sitting with my Joanie, holding hands, quietly enjoying each other's company on the days when I walked her over to this haven of tranquility.

We took the elevator to the second floor.

"We have two breakfast rooms on this floor. If you don't want to go to the main dining room, we have everything you'd need. Yes, available twenty-four seven."

We walked by a small computer room containing two computers and a printer. They'd be handy if mine went on the fritz. The laundry room with four combination washer/dryers plus an ironing board and electric iron was also on this floor.

"We have laundry rooms on each floor," said Val.

Just before the second elevator was the hairdressing salon. It contained plenty of seating for the residents that might want to visit before or after their appointment.

"Let's look at some of our accommodations. I'll take you into different sized rooms and suites. You can decide which suits your needs best."

Val was a professional. She wasn't trying to sell something. She was helping me decide what I needed. Did I mention that I used to be in marketing too?

"Would you like a coffee?"

We were back to our starting point. Val produced some floor plans of the various rooms and suites that we'd visited. A young Filipina appeared with two coffees. She was another smartly-dressed, attractive young woman with another huge smile.

"This is Edlyn, our assistant marketing manager. She's also our relocations coordinator. When you've made your decision to move in, Edlyn will ensure that your transition will be as smooth as silk. Edlyn will coordinate the timing of your move. She'll be here when your furniture arrives. The questions you'll have, Edlyn will answer them all. She'll show you all of the amenities. If you intend to do your own washing, she'll show you how the washing machines work. For the first day or two, Edlyn will have someone show you to your place in the dining room. Yes, she'll even help you pick out a good parking stall in our underground garage."

I'd made my decisions. I knew which suite I wanted and I knew when I'd be moving in. I listened to the rest of Val's presentation.

"I'm pretty sure that I'll be moving in but I'd like a day or two to think it over."

I never made a major decision until I'd slept on it. I called Val the next morning.

"I'll be over at lunchtime with my deposit check. I have plans for the summer so I'd like to move in on the first day of September."

In the loosely translated words of my hero Robert Burns,

"The best laid plans of mice and men often go awry."

Chapter Sixty-seven

As February came to a close, Joan's physical condition worsened. She was transported to the local hospital located just a few minutes from the care center. I arrived as she was being wheeled into the ER. Diagnosed with dehydration and a slight bladder infection, IVs and medication quickly stabilized her condition. Around midnight, it was decided that she could go back to the care center. I kissed her goodnight and left her in the good hands of the paramedics.

"Tell them I'll be there before breakfast."

I arrived home around 1 am.

Joan never properly recovered from this first setback. The sparkle had gone from her eyes. There were only one-way conversations and no more questions. She spent most of the days and nights in bed. The few desultory attempts at walking resulted in near collapse after just a few yards. We resorted to using a wheelchair. Joan showed no interest in the piano. I took her hands and placed them on the keys. Nothing. I was heartbroken, I was losing my Joanie, one of the last two things that gave her pleasure was gone. She would always have me. I vowed to myself that I'd do everything I could to help her maintain her trust in me.

Our attempts to continue to use the dining room ended in failure. Joan just sat, looking forward. If she accepted my spoon-fed offerings, they dribbled out of her mouth when I withdrew the spoon. I arranged that all of her meals would be served in her room. Despite my coaxing and cajoling, she still ate and drank very little.

Doctor Olibanji had told me that when Joan had medical problems, her dementia would worsen. It was no comfort that this worsening resulted in Joan quietly withdrawing from life around her. No more would we endure the noisy shouting, screaming, and verbally abusive behavior that I'd witnessed in the hospital, two short years earlier. I'd prefer that to what I was witnessing now.

One afternoon, about three weeks after Joan's visit to the hospital, after my futile attempts to feed her, I noticed that Joan was less responsive than usual. Her expressionless face was pallid. I called the nurse. She rechecked Joan's blood pressure, which had been low on her first check before lunch, but there was no change.

"I'll check again in a short while. If there's no improvement, I'll call Doctor Olibanji,"

I decided to make a quick trip home for some lunch. My premonitory senses told me that we'd be spending more time in the hospital. The phone was ringing when I arrived home. I was right. Doctor Olibanji had given instructions that Joan be sent to hospital. They were waiting for the ambulance to arrive.

"Have your supper and you'll be able to meet her there."

Again, I arrived at the hospital as Joan was being wheeled in to the ER. I explained to the receptionist that Joan had dementia. The medical staff would require me to be available to supply whatever information they'd need. I was quickly ushered into one of the examination rooms. Joan had a ghastly greyish pallor and wasn't responding to the doctor's questions. I explained what I could about Joan's medical history, her symptoms, the lack of food intake, and the recent changes in her condition.

An IV and oxygen were the immediate needs. An MRI and a chest X-ray were arranged. The X-ray was performed without delay right in the exam room. Modern medical techniques allowed for portable machines to be available wherever and whenever they were needed.

"Please stand behind the wall," said the technician. "You wouldn't want to become sterile, would you?"

Everyone's a comedian.

Within minutes we were wheeling through the corridors. The young porter, jovial and friendly, I was just trying to remain calm. They didn't need me to comfort Joan while she was having the MRI. She was quiet and docile.

"We're going to fit a catheter now. Would you wait outside please," I was told once we were back at the ER. I told them that my presence would be helpful.

"No, wait outside."

Two minutes later, a voice came over the ER speaker system,

"Could we have two available staff to assist in unit 10."

"Told you," I said to myself.

Joanie became quiet after her high decibel protest when her body had been invaded. The doctor diagnosed a severe bladder infection plus dehydration. He was concerned that there was something else that they hadn't yet found. I stayed with Joanie.

"I love you," she mouthed to me.

Around 1 am, the nurse told me to go home. I left after kissing Joan.

"Goodnight, God Bless."

I had another sleepless night worrying about my dear Joanie. Out of bed before 6, I was thankful that I didn't receive the phone call that I'd expected at some time during the night. My plan was to shower, dress, do whatever needed to be done around the house, then breakfast. I'd leave for the hospital around 9.

At 8 am, the phone rang. My pulse started racing. It was the ER doctor. He was just starting his day shift. Joan's condition hadn't improved. She was still unresponsive. Consulting with the previous shift doctor, they hadn't been able to diagnose Joan's ailment. Could I enlighten them on Joan's previous hospital visits? I told him that I'd be with him in fifteen minutes.

Joan was where I'd left her. She was lying quietly, surrounded by two nurses and a doctor.

"Hi, Joanie," I said as I walked in.

"Hi," she replied, looking back at me a little smile on her face.

"That's the first word Joan's spoken since last night," said one of the nurses. "Joan has recognized your voice."

The nurse explained to me that dementia sufferers, when being cared for by one person, place all of their trust in that person.

The doctor asked me to step outside the room. He explained that although Joan's condition had stabilized, they still didn't know the root cause of her sickness.

When she was discharged from the other hospital two years earlier, it had been noted that there was a mass in her abdomen.

"We'll be admitting Joan into the hospital. We'd like to keep our eye on her for a few days."

I spent the rest of the morning sitting with Joan. I got the occasional squeeze of my hand and was encouraged. My Joan's a fighter. She's not giving up that easy.

"Go get something to eat," I was advised around 1 pm. "We'll be moving Joan to the 7th floor later this afternoon."

I did as I was told. I always did.

"Back in an hour."

Chapter Sixty-eight

Unit 72 was a secure haven for patients with dementia and similar disabilities. It was fully staffed with experienced and caring people and everyone was cheerful and smiling. Two nurses introduced themselves.

"Hi, Joan, we'll take good care of you."

Joan showed no interest.

Her room was close to the unit entrance. It was a large room, which she'd be sharing it with an older, rather frail lady called Clare.

"Hi, Clare, I'm Ron. This is Joanie, my wife. She's not feeling too well."

Clare had a surprisingly strong voice for such a frail body.

"Hi, Ron," she said. "Hi, Joanie."

There was no response from Joan.

"She'll say hi when she's feeling better," I explained.

"That's okay."

Joan's condition remained the same throughout the afternoon. Clare's granddaughter, also named Clare, accompanied by her two teenage daughters, arrived for their daily visit. It was a diversion for me as introductory conversation took me away from worrying about my lovely Joan, if only for a short time.

Around 8 pm, Joan seemed a little more comfortable but still not communicating. I asked the nurse if it was okay for me to visit early the next morning.

"We usually have visitors after 11 but you can come at 9, straight after breakfast."

I left, feeling just slightly more optimistic than I'd felt the previous night. My Joanie was in good hands, again.

I was back at the hospital at 8:30 the next day. Joan looked a little better.

"How are you Joanie?" I asked, realizing it was a stupid question.

"Bloody awful."

My Joan was back.

Pureed breakfast was on the bedside tray. The nurses had tried to feed Joan but she'd refused to eat. I worked my magic and coaxed her into taking a few spoonful's of cereal, scrambled egg, and a little milk. The nurses agreed to my suggestion that I arrive earlier the next day. I sat with Joan and she was communicative but not in a conversational way. There was a small greeting for Clare, a little banter with the nurses. I was so relieved to see the improvement.

Later, we had a visit from the attending physician. He noted that Joan had improved but they were still trying to diagnose the cause of her ailment. They'd keep Joan in the hospital for a few days. I was happy with that. Although the care at the care center was good, the professional medical help, always available at the hospital, was a far better option. I stayed with Joan to help her with her lunch. She ate a little more than she had at breakfast. After lunch, while Joan slept, I left for home and my own lunch.

I was back for suppertime and Joan was pleased to see me. We spent a nice couple of hours together with a little conversation. It was more than we had had for a few weeks. The following morning, Joan's breakfast was on the tray when I arrived. A note covered the tray.

"Leave for Ron."

I was amused and flattered.

The eighth morning in the hospital produced an event that will stay with me forever. I arrived in the room on time. Breakfast had been delivered early. Three of the nursing staff were trying unsuccessfully to spoon-feed Joan. Her mouth was tightly shut.

"Good Morning," I said.

Upon seeing me and hearing my voice Joan flung both arms into the air.

"Hey, hey," she yelled.

The sheer joy in her face was something I had never seen in our 57 years together.

"Hey, hey."

Joan was ecstatic. Both arms were in the air again.

"Okay ladies, Joan wants me to help with her breakfast."

A few minutes later, one of the nurses, a Nigerian lady, came back into the room

"I've just phoned my husband about you. You're unbelievable"

"What did I do?" I protested.

Joan was in the hospital for ten days. The care and treatment that she'd received had revived her physically but she wasn't fully recovered. Her dementia had worsened marginally. We couldn't expect more.

Chapter Sixty-nine

It was now late March. I'd resumed my daily routines at Park Place. Each morning, Joan was bathed and cleaned as she lay in bed. I assisted with getting her into positions that were necessary for the caregiver to complete her tasks. Joan's protests were becoming more perfunctory.

Breakfasts, lunches, and suppers were still frustrating for me. My Joanie needed nourishment but she just refused to eat.

We'd still dress Joan even though she'd remain in bed. Some days we took short trips around the unit in a wheelchair. A team of two caregivers would place Joan into the wheelchair with the aid of a portable electronic lifting device. It was brought into the room each morning. She enjoyed the short ride in the lift but was ambivalent about the wheelchair, preferring to drag her feet rather than have them placed in the stirrups. My Joan never did want to do things the easy way.

Prior to Joan being admitted into the Care Centre in January, I had cataract procedures for both eyes scheduled for late March and early April. The need for surgery had become evident when I had my eyes tested prior to renewing my driving license on my 80th birthday. I just squeaked through the test and without vision correction, I'd probably lose my driving license on my 82nd birthday.
On the days of the procedures, I arranged for them to be performed in the late afternoons. I'd be away from Joan's side for the minimum of time.

"I can see clearly now; the clouds have gone."

The singing amused the caregivers. My attempt at humor was for them. I was desperately worried about my Joanie. I could see that she was failing. I felt so helpless. The doctor, the unit manager, and the nurses all visited with Joan and I more frequently. Joan wasn't complaining, she just displayed total lethargy. I was still trying to be upbeat but it was becoming harder. What could I do? I could tell her how much I loved her and I did, repeatedly.

Chapter Seventy

Thursday, April 17th was a dark day, literally and figuratively. It was Maundy Thursday, a day of remembrance. Jesus sat with his disciples and ate his last Passover supper on this day.

In 1210, England's infamous King John, the one that was forced into signing the Magna Carta, was the unwilling participant of the charitable act of distributing alms to the poor of the land. This tradition still continues, albeit more willingly, by British royalty to this day.

Today the sky was overcast and snow was in the forecast. Neither history nor the weather was on my mind as I drove the all too familiar route to the care center. I was thinking of the day ahead. My thoughts weren't optimistic. How could they be? As the elevator door opened on the second floor, I took a deep breath. It was time for my cheerful entrance. Joan was awake.

"Hi, Joanie."

My loud greeting was rewarded by a tiny smile from Joan. There were two kisses this morning.

"Love you, Joanie," I said, as I took off my coat. My chair was where I'd left it the night before. So were the bottles of Ensure and Boost. They were on the nightstand, opened but untouched. Obviously, the caregivers hadn't been able to persuade Joan to drink anything. Emma was Joan's caregiver that day. I was grateful for that. They were all excellent but Emma always expressed that little extra vocal concern.

Breakfast was brought in. My futile attempts to feed Joan resulted in nothing but despair for me. I tried spooning the fortified drinks. Joan ingested enough to give me just a little encouragement.

We didn't try any wheelchair activity that morning. Joan wasn't very responsive. There was only a slight squeeze of my hand as I kissed her or told her that I loved her.

Lunch was a repeat of our breakfast experience. I continued to sit with Joan. I could eat later. I told the nurse that Joan was becoming less responsive. We needed the doctor. Checking Joan's vital signs, the nurse said that she'd call Dr. Olabangi. Knowing it was going to be a long day, around 5 pm I told the nurse that I was going home for a meal and that I'd be back soon.

Halfway through my supper, the nurse phoned. The doctor had told her to get Joan to the hospital. The ambulance had been dispatched and should be at the ER before 7 pm.

It was snowing heavily as I arrived at the hospital and the apparatus to pay for parking wasn't functioning. I wasn't going to mess around with that. I hurried into the ER. I was in the waiting area shortly before the ambulance arrived. The receptionist recognized me from our previous visit.

"Give them a couple of minutes then go through."

Joan was totally unresponsive. One of the nurses was hooking up IVs and oxygen. Another nurse, after applying a gel to Joan's arm, was using an ultrasound device, another modern method to ascertain the strength of Joan's pulse.

"We need to insert a catheter," they said a little later, after blood tests.

There was no discussion. I held Joan's hands and face. She became responsive enough to protest but was soon back to her semiconscious state.

From my chair at Joan's bedside, I could see the ER's control area. Joan's doctor had his eyes fixed to the computer screen. I speculated that he was analyzing the results of Joan's blood tests.

A couple of minutes later, he came and sat beside me.

"You know she's dying."

It wasn't a question.

"She'll probably be gone in a couple of hours."

The doctor's words didn't shock me. My dear Joanie was dying. I didn't say anything. I just looked at him.

"Would you like us to call someone?"

"No," I said. "I'll call my niece later."

I didn't feel any out pouring of grief, no feeling of sorrow. I can't describe how I felt. Possibly a quiet disbelief. Joanie wouldn't see me grieving. My Joanie was still with me. She was in a slightly raised position. Her face was 18 inches away from mine. She was holding my hand.

"I'll stay here."

"I'll be back in a few minutes."

He closed the curtain as he left. I was grateful that I could be alone with my Joan. I kissed her gently on her lips, on her cheeks, on her forehead, then her lips again. I whispered to her that I was with her and I'd always be with her. She squeezed my hand. I kissed her again.

After a couple of minutes, the doctor sat with me.

"She has septicemia of the abdomen. It's spreading to her vital organs."

It was good that he kept talking. I wouldn't be able to say anything sensible.

"We've read Joan's Personal Directive and my colleague and I agree."

Joan and I had both chosen, some years earlier, that no heroic measures were to be attempted if we were to became terminal.

"Even if we were to act against her wishes, and perform surgery, it's a thousand-to-one odds against it being successful. If we were to succeed, Joan's life wouldn't improve."

I nodded.

"We'll withdraw her medication. It's no longer effective. We'll also cease administering the IV. If we don't, the fluid will enter her lungs and she'll drown. We'll continue with the oxygen and we'll start delivering pain medication. The dosage will be at your direction. If you feel that Joan's in any pain at all, we'll increase the dosage."

All this was delivered in a conversational manner. No unneeded soothing. Not unfeeling either. He must have been through this many times before. He was a good man.

A nurse quietly removed some of the paraphernalia from the IV stand. She left as quietly as she'd entered.

I was alone with Joan again. I told her how much I loved her. How much I'd always loved her. How much I always would love her. Each sentence punctuated with a gentle kiss on her lips.

My Joan was quiet and peaceful. No signs of dementia. What a blessing. The nurse swished the curtain to one side.

"We're moving Joan to a quieter area of the ER."

I hadn't noticed the noise. Now I could hear the groans of the people in pain. The loud voices of the nurses asking the questions they needed to ask. The rattling of the gurneys as patients were being transferred to and from the examining rooms increased the decibel level in this busy part of the unit.

As the nurses prepared Joan for the move, I took the opportunity to phone Chris. Joan wouldn't be alone in the short time I was away. Chris asked if she should come over. I told her not to and that I'd call her around 6 am. I was back with Joan as she was wheeled to the quietest part of the unit.

A different nurse introduced herself. She made Joan comfortable, raising the bed to allow Joan and I to be on the same eye level.

"Do you need anything? A glass of water? Here's some sponges to moisten Joan's lips with. Here's the call button."

She left us alone. No, we weren't alone. We were together.

Every few minutes, I could see the silhouette of the doctor near the edge of the curtain. He was being very discreet with his monitoring.

About 3:30 am, I was holding both of Joan's hands.

"We all live in a yellow submarine, a yellow submarine, a yellow submarine."

I was gently moving her hands in time with my quiet singing. She gave me a tiny smile. She was saying something.

"Hi, sweetie, you're awake." I said, trying to sound normal.

The nurse must have heard my voice.

"I think Joanie wants to say hi," I said.

"Hi, Joanie."

Joan answered with a tiny "Hi."

The nurse checked her vital signs and left. Returning a minute or two later, she informed me that they were moving Joan up to the 9th floor. On one of our previous visits to the hospital, I'd learned that the palliative care unit was situated on that level.

At 4 am, we were greeted by the night nurse and her aide, both smiling and cheerfully efficient.

"We'll soon get you settled in, Joanie."

The activity seemed to have energized Joan a little. She was quietly talking to me but not saying anything that I could understand.

"That's right, Joanie, don't worry, we can settle down now."

My answer seemed to be the right one. We resumed our hand holding with me kissing her every half minute or so. The responsive slight pursing of her lips gave me a glimmer of hope that my Joanie was coming back to me.

Around 6 am, the nursing shift changed. The day nurse, Carol, gave me access to a cell phone. I was able to call Chris without leaving the room. She told me that she and Rob were coming to visit. They arrived at 7am. I gave them a quick update and they had a quiet word with Joan,

"Back in five minutes, Joanie. Talk to Chris. Don't go anywhere. Love you."

Chris took my chair by the bed and held her Auntie Joan's hand.

With Rob driving, I gave him a more detailed description of the night's events. When we got home, I had a shower, grabbed a change of clothes and had a quick breakfast. We were back at Joan's bedside within an hour. I'd hated to leave Chris with Joan. I didn't want her to have to deal with the possibility of Joan passing while they were alone. Chris and Joan were both fine.

"We had a chat. Joan waved her arms a little. Everything's good."

Chris was so grounded. She and Rob were my anchors. After hugs, they were off to work with a request that I call them later. They promised that they'd visit early the next day.

Joan's nurse and her aide were in and out of our room at regular intervals. They were always gentle and respectful. They cleaned and changed Joan while I held her face and hands. They repositioned her to keep her comfortable. The routines had become so familiar since Joan entered into care three months earlier. Now, Joan didn't struggle or protest.

When I thought Joan was experiencing pain, I asked the nurse to increase the medication a little. It was administered by a shunt in Joan's thigh. It didn't appear to be uncomfortable and Joan didn't seem to be aware of it.

The palliative care doctor visited. Another lovely lady, she asked how long we'd been married. What beautiful memories we must have shared. How I'll cherish those memories. She asked us about our family. Did we have children? I told her about our wonderfully supportive extended family. Do we have spiritual beliefs? Were we churchgoers? She wasn't intrusive. Every word she spoke was genuinely coming from her heart. She said I needed to rest. I replied that there will be plenty of time later.

"I know we have a very comfortable armchair somewhere. I'll find it and have someone bring it here."

Did I need anything? I left Joan's side briefly as the good doctor hugged me before she left.

Joanie's breathing was still being assisted by the oxygen. Occasionally she'd gasp a little and my anxiety level would shoot up. Then Joan was back to normal and we were both breathing easier. Joan seemed to have forgotten how to close her eyes. Now they remained open, unblinking. I didn't wish for them to close. It might be forever.

I talked to Joan about how I loved her beautiful smile. How much I loved her and how much she loved me. The occasional squeezing of my hand and puckering of her lips signaled that it was time for another kiss. I'd talk about our eventful life together. The memories. The laughs we'd shared. The places we'd been. The wonderful friends we'd collected in our travels. The occasional raising of an eyebrow signaled I should give it a rest. My Joanie still had a sense of humor.

Around 1 pm the unit's department head, Doctor Ali, visited with us. He was another gentle man. He didn't examine Joan and I realized that he didn't need to. He commiserated with me, asking the same the questions his staff doctor had asked.

"Do you have any questions?"

I asked him if Joan's condition was, in any way, contagious, which it wasn't. I didn't need to ask that stupid question. I just needed to get to my next questions. What procedures take place when Joan expires? Where will Joan be taken to? What do I need to do? How long did he think Joan would stay with us?

I don't know how I held myself together as I asked the questions and processed the answers. The last question wasn't answerable.

"Your wife has an extremely strong heart."

At 2 pm, I asked the nurse's aide to stay with Joan while I made a quick trip to the basement cafeteria. I needed to pick up something to eat. I could do without sleep but I knew I had to eat. The elevator whizzed down the 9 floors. I picked up a ready meal, paid for it and was quickly back to the elevator. The trip up was a lot slower, disgorging staff and visitors at each floor. I ate my chef's salad sitting in the lounge chair that had been positioned at Joan's bedside in the few minutes I'd been gone.

At 3 pm, the nurses shift changed and Carol came in to say goodbye.

"We'll see you tomorrow?" I asked.

"No, I'm off for the Easter weekend."

It really was goodbye. We hugged.

Joan's room was spacious with a separate bathroom. Two bedside tables held all the stuff that we needed to keep Joan as comfortable as possible. I was given an aerosol spray to keep Joan's mouth and lips moist. The sponge lollipops might allow water to enter her throat and cause choking. I moved the recliner to one side. It was comfortable but I couldn't hold Joan's hand or kiss her when I was seated.

Good Friday afternoon dragged on. I was still holding Joan's hand. Lots of kisses, on her cheeks, forehead, lips. There was still a little pucker when it was the lips' turn. Joan was always looking at me. I was looking into her eyes, telling her how beautiful they were.

"Oh," I thought. "How I wish I knew what was going on behind those lovely brown eyes."

I called Chris in the early evening.

"Auntie Joan's still with us. She's not in pain."

"Good. Please get some rest. We'll see you in the morning."

Around 7 pm. I decided I needed to eat again. The nurse's aide sat with Joan while I made my dash to the cafeteria.

It's hard to describe my state of mind as the night wore on. Sleep deprivation was causing me to feel that I was outside of myself looking in. I was sitting in the hard-backed chair that allowed me to be close to Joan. I had to keep my Joan comfortable in her mind. The nurses would keep her body comfortable.

When I wasn't kissing her, I was telling Joan how much I loved her. I spoke of the wonderful memories.

"Remember Hawaii? The Charthouse? The lovely music? We swam in the ocean."

I was reliving those lovely times. Joan was content to hear my voice, comforted to know that her Ronnie was by her side.

Sometime after midnight, I sat back, my eyes closed. Sleep was about to take over. I felt a gentle tugging at the front of my shirt. I opened my eyes. It was Joan. When she saw my eyes were open, she put her fingers towards her lips. She wanted another kiss. God got us through that long night.

Activity outside of the room signaled Saturday morning's shift change. Around 6 am, Shea, our new day nurse, introduced herself. She was another lovely young lady with a demeanor that was well suited for her calling.

I always tried to project an 'in control' image with the nursing staff. They all knew that I was close to losing it but they played along.

"When's the big day?" I asked, noticing that Shea was pregnant.

"A couple of months yet," she replied, smiling.

I explained that my niece would be coming in at 7am to enable me to go home and do what I had to do to prepare for the day. Shea said she'd stay close. I didn't have to worry about leaving Chris with Joan.

Chris and Rob arrived on time, hugs and another quick update. I introduced Shea, who had the same name as Chris and Rob's five-year-old granddaughter. I kissed Joan.

"I'll be back in a couple of minutes, Joanie. Don't go anywhere. Love you."

I kissed her again.

The drive home was a little faster since there was less traffic on Saturday mornings. Rob tried to distract me by talking about events at his workplace. It didn't work. I needed to talk about Joan. He made some scrambled eggs, toast, and coffee while I took another quick shower and changed into fresh clothes. I drank the coffee as we drove back to the hospital.

Chris was relieved to see us. Auntie Joan had spoken a little but Chris didn't understand what she said. I thought that Joan had probably been asking where I was but I didn't say anything. Hugs were exchanged before Chris and Rob left.

"We'll pop in this afternoon. See you then."

I was back in my seat talking to Joan, holding her hand. As always, she was looking at me.

"I love you, Joanie."

There was a slight little movement of her hand. I kept talking and kissing all morning. Joanie still needed to know that her Ronnie was by her side. When Shea and her helper came in to attend to Joan, I held her face in my hands. They changed her position every couple of hours. This enabled Joan to be comfortable. It also displayed their dedication to their patient. At noon there was a pretend knock on the curtain.

"Knock knock."

It was always closed when Joan and I were alone. Marg, Chris's sister, was there with her husband, Paul.

"Hi, Uncle Ron."

She was the only one of our many nieces and nephews that didn't call me Uncle Ronnie.

"If we phoned, you'd tell us not to come, so we didn't phone."

More hugs. I was really pleased to see them. They are a lovely couple. Practicing Christians, they run Entheos, a pastoral retreat and conference center. It was set in idyllic surroundings just a few miles west of Calgary. They never pushed their beliefs onto me. They understood that I thought God was good. That was all the religion that I needed. We chatted, including Joan in the conversation.

A short time later, Chris and Rob joined us. There more hugs followed by more quiet conversations. The family group didn't stay long. They knew that my time with Joan was precious.

My thoughts went towards our wonderfully supportive friends, Ralph and Lucille. It was time that I told them the sad news. Best to do it now. I walked into the bathroom, leaving the door open. Joan could see me although I didn't think that she could hear me. Lucille answered the phone. I sensed her reaction as I related the events of the last few days and the seriousness of Joan's condition.

Lucille's voice was breaking as she expressed her sorrow. She was concerned, as always, about me and my wellbeing. No, I didn't want them to come into town.

"Remember Joanie as you last saw her."

She thanked me, telling me to give kisses to Joanie from her and Ralph. I said I'd do that right away. Holding Joan's hands once more, I told her that Lucille and Ralph sent their love.

"They've sent kisses too. Here's one from me. Here's one from Lucille. Here's one from Ralph." There was a little pursing of her lips for Ralph, her pretend archenemy.

It was time for me to eat. Shea said that she'd sit with Joan. I returned quickly with another chef's salad. A little later it was time for another shift change. Shea came in to say goodnight.

"Working tomorrow?"

"Yes, I'll be here at six."

We exchanged hugs just in case. The late shift nurse came in to check on Joan and I. My sleep deprivation must have been evident.

"You must get some rest."

"Easy for you to say," was my unspoken and unnecessary response.

Saturday evening wore on. Joan looked at me and I looked right back. She seemed so peaceful. No grimaces. No groans. I couldn't hear her breathing, just the irregular clicking of the oxygen equipment. Joan still needed to know that I was with her. I was holding her hand.

"I love you, Joanie. God bless you, Joanie"

"Yesterday, all my troubles seemed so far away, now it looks as though they're here to stay, oh I believe in yesterday"

I sang softly. I don't know how, but I knew all of the words.

"Suddenly, I'm not half the man I used to be, there's a shadow hanging over me, oh yesterday came suddenly. Why she had to go, I don't know she wouldn't say. I said something wrong, now I long for yesterday. Yesterday, love was such an easy game to play, now I need a place to hide away, oh I believe in yesterday."

Lennon and McCartney wrote that beautifully sad ballad just for me and my Joanie.

We got through Saturday night. I'd talked a lot, repeating all the memories I spoke of on the previous night. I quietly crooned some of the other songs that Joan loved. Her breathing remained shallow. A couple of times during the long night, I thought I'd lost her. A slight movement in her eyes told me that she was still with me.

At 6 am on Sunday morning Shea came into the room to perform the necessary check of Joan's vital signs. This time, there was no small talk, just a little touch on my shoulder. Chris and Rob arrived promptly at 7 while Shea was in the room.

"Don't worry. I'll be here if Chris needs me."

"Back in five minutes, Joanie. Don't go any-where. Love you."

This time I added something else.

"God Bless."

Rob had parked close to the entrance. We arrived at home very quickly. A fast shower, fresh clothes. Toast and coffee to go. Then we were back in the car and back in the hospital. Chris, looking really tense, was relieved that we'd returned so quickly. She knew, as I did, that her lovely Auntie Joanie would be gone from us soon. We said our goodbyes. Chris kissed her Auntie Joan. There was no mention of tomorrow.

"I'll call you later," I simply said.

Joan and I together. The curtain drawn. I was leaning really close to Joan's face, holding her hand. She looked tranquil. No anxiety, no fear. I never got tired of saying how much I loved her. I never got tired of kissing her on her forehead, on her cheeks, and on her lips.

"God bless you, Joanie," I now said, after every kiss.

Shea's aide came in to reposition Joan. I waved him away without speaking. He understood.

"It's okay, Joanie. Your mom and dad are waiting for you. You're lovely Georgie too. Don't be afraid. I'll see you later. When God sends for me. I'll be with you again. I'll always love you, Joanie. God bless."

"For this is the Kingdom of Heaven and here on the threshold we stand, pass through the portals now, we'll be immortal now, hold my hand."

I couldn't sing the words of the song we had danced to on the day we met so many years ago. I couldn't even say them. A short time later, Shea came quietly into the room.

"I think she's gone," I said.

Shea checked Joan's chest and throat areas with her stethoscope.

"Joan's gone."

"Would you close her eyes?" I asked.

"Yes, of course."

Walking around to my side of the bed, Shea put her hand on my shoulder.

"I'll give you some time alone."

I kissed Joan.

"Goodbye, God bless."

I wept. The tears that I'd been holding back for so long came streaming out of my eyes. The grief that I felt was something I'd never experienced before.

I wept for myself. My Joanie was in a better place.

My Joanie died peacefully, as I was holding her hand, at 11 minutes past 11 on Easter Sunday morning, April 20, 2014.

God had given my Joanie and me our time to say goodbye.

Addendum

Although I have no professional education on the subject, I feel that my ten-year journey through dementia with my lovely Joanie, qualifies me to offer advice to the family caregivers of loved ones who suffer with this debilitating condition.

Before I start, I hope you have sought professional advice on ascertaining your loved one's condition. It is important that you do not feel that there is a stigma attached to dementia. It is a disease of the brain, pure and simple. Not having it diagnosed, does not mean that it does not exist. Denial does not delay its progression.

I do understand that the behavior of dementia sufferers will vary according to the type of dementia with which they are inflicted. The part of the brain that is affected by dementia, dictates what behavioral traits will become evident.

From my experience, I believe that the ability of the caregiver to communicate their feelings to their loved one is a big factor in being able to live through what Michaelle Jean, one of Canada's past Governor Generals, described in an essay, as an insidious fog. Her mother had dementia.

Your first questions. How will I cope? How will I know what to do?

My first answer. From the first day of learning of your loved one's illness, you will learn to cope. You will learn what to say and what to do, and, more importantly, you will learn what not to say and what not to do.

Short term memory loss is one of the first symptoms of early onset dementia. Your loved one will often repeat questions or statements. For instance, "What day is it today?" If you feel exasperated hearing the question repeated and answer "I've just told you." Your voice and body language will cause your loved one to become aggressive and hostile. Pretty soon, both of you will feel ill tempered and a very poor tone will be set. A stony silence will hurt you more than your loved one. I found it easier to answer the repeated question with a good humored reply. "It's Wednesday, all day and its Thursday all day tomorrow." My voice indicated that everything was fine, nothing to worry about. What did it cost me to repeat my answer each time the question was asked? Nothing, absolutely nothing.

We're all human, there will be times when you are not at your best and lose patience with your loved one. He or she will forget your squabble in a moment, their lack of short term memory will ensure that. The harsh words you both may have shared, will be with you for a long time. That's something for you to think about. Bite your tongue when you can't say something nice, you'll be the benefactor.

Next question. What should we do about irrational behavior?

Tolerate it with good humor. Try to keep every situation on an even keel. Once again, your voice and your body language will dictate the mood of the moment.

Don't forget, your goal will be to get through each day as best you can. If your loved one is content to spend their days doing little things that make no sense to you but are of interest to them, go with the flow. That should be your mantra, go with the flow.

In my story, I mention an incident when Joan, using scissors, cut twenty, five dollar bills in half. Her thinking was probably, that she would double her money, her smile when she showed me her handiwork was just lovely. How could I be mad at my Joanie. I was genuinely amused as I did the repair work.

You will learn that trinkets become treasures, things of little value become very precious. Many quiet hours can be spent just touching them. Encourage your loved one, show them that you share the love of their possessions. You may see it as an obsession, think of it as a pastime. Quiet times with a dementia sufferer are a blessing.

Some of the best days of my life were spent sitting with my Joanie, me, talking about good times in the past, Joan listening. I could tell if she was really remembering just by her comments. Sometimes she was, sometimes she wasn't. It didn't make any difference, we were happy together, I learned that the precious memories I spoke of were therapeutic for me and comforting for Joan.

I discovered that Joan's dementia became the focus of my life. I woke up each morning knowing that my day would be spent caring for Joan and ministering to her needs. I would go to sleep knowing that we had got through another day together.

Despair is an ugly word, please don't let it into your thoughts. There will be good times to compensate for the times that are difficult. I tried to recall special memories of happy days each time I felt low. You might feel resentment. Why you? This is where your love will be tested. In my case, I remembered one of our wedding vows. "In sickness and in health." I'm sure my Joan would have stayed in love with me and taken care of me if our roles were reversed.

You will learn not to ask questions. Questions require thought process, something that is difficult. Instead, use conversation to obtain answers that you need. "I wonder what we should have to eat?" will produce a better response than "What do you want to eat?"

When dressing Joan each morning, I would lay different items on the bed and declare. "I think you should wear this outfit today." Joan's response was always to choose the other one. So that's the one she wore. An example of reverse psychology that worked every time.

Personal hygiene for a dementia sufferer is difficult but necessary to maintain. It is equally difficult for me to prescribe solutions or easy fixes, there aren't any. In our case, Joan's modesty ensured that we would have a pitched battle every step of the way. The battles would be forgotten soon, so I did what I had to do.

In the early stages of Joan's dementia, I noticed that my Joanie became an expert in trying to disguise her condition. She was aware that she forgot things or made missteps when trying to perform everyday tasks. I learned not to question her explanations. I pretended not to notice when she poured her orange juice into her Raisin Bran. The next morning, I suggested that she drink her juice, because I'd already put milk into her cereal. How easy was that? I could have made a big deal of it. What would have been achieved? That saucepan that had been on the stove too long? It was easier for me to scour it than scold Joan for being forgetful.

Something that gave me pleasure was the way Joan behaved in social occasions when she was around people other than myself. She greeted everyone as though they were the best of friends. She didn't distinguish between store clerks and medical specialists, everyone was a recipient of her charm and warm smile. I was careful not to interfere with her interactions. The puzzled looks that I sometimes received from people meeting Joan for the first time were priceless. I occasionally used the phrase, cognitive degeneration, to explain anything inappropriate that Joan may have said or done. Joan never reacted negatively. I dread to think what would she have said, had I used the words, dementia or Alzheimer's.

Social interaction was important to me. We needed to maintain contact with family and friends. A support group is important, necessary and can never be too large.

When with friends, Joan was always in the forefront, she was no shrinking violet. Everyone had fun with her. They understood and ignored Joan's social missteps. There was never a need to apologize or attempt to explain away her dementia inspired, irrational behavior. It's a sickness. Would you apologize for having a broken leg or breast cancer? There are still a lot of people in our world that do not know how to conduct social intercourse with dementia sufferers, I know one lady who used to talk to Joan in a loud voice, perhaps she thought Joan might understand her better. It distressed me when some people would whisper to me in Joan's presence, usually, they'd tell me of someone they know with the same condition. Were they trying to console me or just making conversation? Caregivers need friends to socialize with and help take their minds away from their everyday situation.

As Joan's dementia progressed, her behavioural pattern changed. I had to learn new skills. Our family doctor was my mentor. I recommend that all family caregivers keep in close contact with their GPs. If their doctor does not have experience with geriatric care, I suggest that experts be consulted. I was fortunate, our doctor's special interest was geriatrics. He insisted that we visited him each month. Each visit garnered valuable advice. He explained that 'White lies' and promises that you can't keep were okay. Constantly repeated requests by your loved one, for something not possible, will be easily be assuaged by saying that "We'll do it tomorrow." or something similar. The request will be forgotten tomorrow. No harm done. Keep your loved one as happy as possible was our doctor's major message.

Secrecy and distrust became part of our lives. Joan would hide her money, her favorite pieces of jewelry, house keys and my car keys. I tried to analyze why she would act in this fashion, the best I could come up with, was perhaps she felt a lack of security, perhaps she was afraid of losing her possessions and her home. Of course, I never discussed her irrational actions with her. Would discussion alter her behaviour? Not at all. Joan's lack of memory ensured that she would forget where she hid everything. Once, I spent two full days, looking for a pair of gold ear rings without success They were a gift from Joan's grandmother. I turned the house upside down, those precious heirlooms were gone. Two months later, they showed up amongst Joan's treasures. Another two months later, they disappeared again. I never found them.

I was fortunate that Joan maintained a healthy appetite for most of our journey. I had heard stories of dementia sufferers not wanting to eat and becoming frail. Joan was the opposite, often asking. "When are we having lunch?" thirty minutes after she'd just eaten. Initially, an unpleasant discussion would ensue. "Are you trying to starve me?" I learned to serve half of her meal, then give her the other half when she asked. Peace restored. I kept our meals to a regular schedule as I did with most of the routine things we did in our, now restricted life style. Anything out of the usual pattern invoked question and confusion. Why risk it?

I'm not sure that I can call it good fortune, but Joan's arthritic condition and the pain associated with it, was a deterrent to any wandering, a common dementia symptom. I never had to go searching around the neigh-borhood, I thank God for that.

Throughout this addendum, I've referred to de-mentia sufferers. I'm pretty sure that the family caregiv-ers are the real sufferers. People with advanced dementia have no memory, every event, be it a conversation or an activity, is what it is, a new chapter in their confused lives. If the caregiver can infuse love into their voice and body language, they will bring their loved one closer. Hugs, kisses, hand holding and expressions of love will induce a long lasting bond that results in absolute trust. I was made aware of this and rewarded by it in an incident that I relate in my story. My Joan responded to my voice and became animated after being silent and unresponsive for more than twelve hours in a hospital emergency unit.

I made many missteps along our long and winding road. I wish I could retrace and replace them. I hope some of my words will help you avoid the pitfalls that were part of our journey. My biggest error was, not seeking help in a timely fashion. As the years ticked by, I had become adamant that I was the only one that Joan would accept as a caregiver companion. I continually de-clined all of the offers of help from friends and family. My love for Joan made me blind to my own welfare. I was sacrificing my own health and wellbeing by taking the sole responsibility of caring for Joan. I know now that I was wrong. Our family doctor recognised that I needed to get professional caregivers involved in Joan's daily life. His advice led me to the actions that I should have taken years earlier.

My advice to all family caregivers is please ac-cept all the help offered to share the care of your loved one. I should have taken advantage of the Alberta Health Service a lot sooner. The Home Care services that are available will enable you to grab a few hours of respite. You will find that you can entrust your loved one to a professional's care and know that your loved one will be in good hands.

In conclusion, I should explain why I decided to tell my story. In my book, I wrote of my intention to move to Trinity Lodge, a retirement residence, to be close to Joan after she was placed into a continuous care centre. Tragically, my Joanie died before I could make the move. When I did move in, four months after Joan passed, I knew that my grief would only worsen if I didn't have something to occupy my mind. I decided to immerse myself in writing about my love for Joan and of the grief that I felt when I lost her. I have no knowledge of the grief that other people feel when they lose their loved one, I could share their sadness but I could never gauge the depth of their grief. I decided that I would express my sorrow, intending to share my writing with family and friends.

I began by relating the events that started on Maundy Thursday, and ended on Easter Sunday. As I wrote, I released a torrent of grief from within me. I drove myself to get to the tragic end. I wrote of talking to Joan as I watched her drift away from me, I spoke of the wonderful life that we had shared. As I read what I had written, I realized that my self imposed task had resulted in a tremendous cathartic reaction. I was gripped by warm thoughts of all the wonderful things that had happened throughout our time together. It was then that I decided that I would share our life with everyone.

The Alzheimer Society of Calgary is grateful to the author, Ron Freckleton, for his generous commitment of all royalties from print and e-book versions of this book to our Society. These funds will help us reach out to even more people impacted by Alzheimer's disease and other forms of dementia.

The Alzheimer Society of Calgary provides vital support, education and care to local impacted individuals and their loved ones. More information is available on our web site.

http://www.alzheimercalgary.ca

64821645R00179

Made in the USA
Charleston, SC
14 December 2016